Field Studies 6 (1987), 695–766

NTRE

A KEY TO THE MAJOR G
TERRESTRIAL IN\

By S. M. TILLING

Field Studies Council, Leonard Wills Field Centre, Nettlecombe Court, Williton, Taunton, Somerset TA4 4HT

CONTENTS

INTRODUCTION

ONE OF THE most frustrating of problems facing biologists who are attempting serious survey work for the first time is knowing where to start in describing and interpreting their data. Untangling the diversity of animals encountered in terrestrial habitats may seem a daunting task, but it is usually possible with sufficient commitment and patience. Identification, an integral part of such work, may seem the most difficult obstacle, particularly when dealing with small invertebrates. Frequently, this is due to the absence of a simple key rather than to any insuperable taxonomic problems. This key has been written with beginners in mind and should help to minimise the problems in identification. A preliminary draft—the "test" version—was subjected to extended trials by a wide range of readers, and this version has been revised in the light of their comments. However, no key is flawless and problems will undoubtedly exist in this version. The AIDGAP project's co-ordinator would welcome suggestions which could be incorporated in any future editions.

All terrestrial invertebrates larger than 1 mm found in the British Isles—any many that are smaller—are included and identification is based on external characters which are visible with a hand lens, or a low-power binocular microscope. I have chosen to interpret the key's title very loosely. Thus, the *major groups* included here encompass several that are not strictly "native" to the *British* Isles, but which may be encountered nevertheless—scorpions and stick insects, for example. Many animals which are predominantly parasitic, or otherwise narrowly restricted by their mode of life, are included because they will be collected using conventional sampling techniques. Invertebrates that are found exclusively in marine or freshwater habitats are omitted, but groups that live predominantly in such environments but are found occasionally in *terrestrial* habitats are covered. However, habitat-based separations are notoriously difficult and readers may feel that additional groups should be included. The AIDGAP project would be interested in any such suggestions, or others that may help to improve the key.

It should be possible to identify most invertebrates without killing them. Remember that many are now protected by law and conservation should always be a priority. One way in which small individuals can be observed without killing is by using a specially manufactured "bug box". This consists of a small transparent dish (a petri dish, for example), inlaid with a perspex sheet which has different diameter holes drilled through it. Animals can be placed in the appropriate-sized recess and the lid replaced. By turning the dish over, the upper and lower surface of the specimen can be examined. Another method is to confine the animal to the corner of a perspex box or dish by using a piece of tissue or plasticine pressed into place.

Many smaller invertebrates can be temporarily "stunned" by placing them in a refrigerator—but not for too long!

A set of notes is given for each group at the back of the guide and these will provide an introduction to the ecology of the animals, whilst the lists of references will enable the reader to continue with further research and identification.

How to Use the Key

The key is arranged in the traditional dichotomous form. At each stage readers have to make a choice between two contrasting descriptions. Depending on their choice, they will be directed either to the name of the taxonomic group or to another couplet in the key. Readers who are unfamiliar with the layout of the guide should always start at couplet A1 in KEY A and read both descriptions before proceeding to the next stage. For example, if in couplet A1 you have decided that the animal has jointed legs go to couplet A2; if the creature has three pairs of jointed legs go to couplet A3; and so on. Eventually, you will be directed to a new key. At times, you may go backwards, but persevere and you will arrive at an answer.

The Illustrations. Wherever possible the illustrations are taken from living and preserved specimens. However, many of the drawings are stylised, to give a composite impression of a group's appearance and will, therefore, not closely resemble the identified specimens. This is inevitable in groups which may contain several thousand species. Some experts will blanch when seeing the caricatures of their chosen group. My only excuse is that the keys are aimed at those with little or no experience. If in doubt, consult one of the texts given in the notes at the back of the guide; the books by Chinery (1986), dealing with adult insects, and Cloudsley-Thompson & Sankey (1961), dealing with non-insect groups, are comprehensive and are particularly useful.

Please Read the Information Notes. These are included throughout the key and will help you in making decisions. You will find that you need to refer to these less and less as your expertise increases. Readers who have used the guide several times will be able to go directly to the appropriate key. When identification has been accomplished go to the back of the guide; the notes given there should confirm your identification, or will help in spotting any obvious discrepancies.

Warning. Beware of damaged specimens. Invertebrates are usually very fragile, and may easily loose appendages—tails, antennae, etc. Critical parts of the keys are highlighted by notes in the text, but try not to mis-handle the animals.

The following table lists the groups which are included in the key. The italicised script indicates the taxonomic level to which each group is taken (see the general notes on taxonomy, p. 746)

Phylum	Class	Order	Sub-order
ASCHELMINTHES	*Nematoda*		
	Nematomorpha		
PLATYHELMINTHES	*Turbellaria*		
NEMERTEA			
ANNELIDA	*Hirudinea*		
	Oligochaeta		
ARTHROPODA	Arachnida	*Scorpionida*	
		Pseudoscorpionida	
		Araneae	
		Opiliones	
		Acari	
	Crustacea	*Isopoda*	
		Amphipoda	
		Copepoda	
	Pauropoda		
	Diplopoda	Chordeumatida	*Craspedosomatidea*
			Chordeumatidea
		Glomerida	
		Polydesmida	
		Polyzoniida	
		Polyxenida	
	Chilopoda	*Geophilomorpha*	
		Lithobiomorpha	
		Scolopendromorpha	
	Symphyla		
	Insecta	*Protura*	
		Thysanura	
		Diplura	
		Collembola	
		Ephemeroptera	
		Odonata	*Zygoptera*
			Anisoptera
		Plecoptera	
		Phasmida	
		Dermaptera	
		Dictyoptera	
		Orthoptera	
		Psocoptera	
		Phthiraptera	*Mallophaga*
			Anoplura
		Hemiptera	
		Thysanoptera	
		Neuroptera	
		Megaloptera	
		Mecoptera	
		Lepidoptera	
		Trichoptera	
		Diptera	
		Siphonaptera	
		Hymenoptera	*Symphyta*
			Apocrita
		Coleoptera	
		Strepsiptera	
MOLLUSCA	Gastropoda	*Prosobranchia*	
		Pulmonata	

GLOSSARY

ABDOMEN. One of the major body divisions; lying behind the head and thorax in insects. Usually carrying the digestive and reproductive organs.

ANTENNA (pl. *Antennae*). Modified front appendage, carrying sensory structures.

ALATE. With wings.

APTEROUS. Lacking wings.

BIFURCATE. Splitting into two branches.

BILOBED. With two lobes.

BRACHYPTEROUS. Short-winged.

CARAPACE. The shield-like structure which covers the head and thorax in arachnids and crustaceans.

CHRYSALIS. The hardened pupal case in metamorphosing insects (see ENDOPTERYGOTA below).

CLITELLUM. A band of enlarged fused segments in earthworms; a source of mucous for protecting eggs and nourishing embryos.

CONIFEROUS. Cone-bearing trees, often characterised by needle-like leaves (e.g. pine needles).

COXA (pl. *Coxae*). A segment of the leg, closest to the body (see Figure 1).

DECIDUOUS. Trees, mainly broad-leaved, that lose their leaves in the winter.

DISTAL. The end of an appendage which is outermost from the body.

DORSAL. The upper surface.

ELYTRON (pl. *Elytra*). The modified front wing of an insect, forming a hardened or leathery protective case for the membranous hind wing which is used for flight and is usually folded underneath. In some insects the elytra may be short, whilst in others they may be fused together (in which case the insect has lost the ability to fly).

ENCYSTING. Forming a protective case, often within a gelatinous coat. This is usually a dormant stage during which development is suspended, and often functions as a protection against adverse conditions.

ENDOPTERYGOTA. The more advanced of the winged insects; undergo a rapid metamorphosis. The wings develop internally in the larva which enters a pupal stage during which it metamorphoses into the adult.

EXOPTERYGOTA. The more primitive of the winged insects; undergo a gradual metamorphosis in which the wings develop externally on the nymph which, in most groups, looks increasingly like the adult as it undergoes a series of moults.

FEMUR. One of the segments of the arthropod leg—see Figure 1.

FLAGELLUM. The delicate hair-like extension of an antenna, usually arising from two or three thickened basal segments.

FORCIPULE. A claw, formed by the modified front leg of a centipede.

HALTERE. Modified insect wing, reduced to a small drumstick-shaped organ which helps to balance the animal in flight.

HEAD. One of the major body divisions. Lying at the front of the body; usually carrying the major neural organs, most advanced sense organs (although this is not always the case) and mouthparts.

HEAD CAPSULE. Usually used to describe a larval/nymphal head which is encapsulated in a hard chitinous case, usually with external palps and other mouthparts, and antennae. This contrasts with the larvae of some advanced insects in which the head capsule has been lost and most external appendages are vestigial or have become enclosed in the fleshy head which can often be retracted into the body behind.

JOINTED LEGS. The "true" legs which arise from the thorax; not to be confused with abdominal prolegs (see below).

LARVA (pl. *Larvae*). The immature stage of arthropods which undergo a complete metamorphosis, i.e. where there is no resemblance to the adult. For terrestrial arthropod groups this refers mainly to the juveniles of the endopterygote insects. The larval stage is followed by pupation during which the animal undergoes the often striking transformation into the adult form.

LATERALLY COMPRESSED. Flattened from side-to-side.

MEMBRANOUS. Transparent and fragile, in contrast to much of the exoskeleton of most arthropods which consists of tough and deeply pigmented cuticle.

MESOTHORAX. The middle (second) of the three thoracic segments (see THORAX).

METATHORAX. The hind-most of the three thoracic segments (see THORAX).

NECK. The junction between the head and the thorax.

NYMPH. The immature stage of arthropods which do not undergo complete metamorphosis, i.e. the majority of the arthropods, excluding the endopterygote winged insects. The nymphs increasingly resemble the adults as they undergo a series of moults (gradual metamorphosis).

PALP. A segmented mouthpart, usually carrying chemo-sensitive cells (the arthropods' equivalent of the taste-buds).

PEDICEL. The narrow waist separating the fused head and thorax (cf. cephalothorax) from the abdomen in spiders, and the thorax and abdomen in Hymenoptera (although it is in fact the modified second abdominal segment in these insects).

PEDIPALP. Segmented structure in arachnids, usually held in front of the head. It may appear leg-like, or can be modified into claws in scorpions and pseudoscorpions or into a sperm transferring organ in male spiders.

PHORESY. Behaviour whereby an animal attaches itself to another animal for purposes of transport, i.e. hitching a lift.

PROBOSCIS. Usually refers to the sucking tube-like mouthparts in bugs (order Hemiptera), but is sometimes used incorrectly to describe any snout-like feature projecting from the front of the head (see ROSTRUM).

PROLEG. A fleshy abdominal appendage found on caterpillars and other insect larvae. Although prolegs may be quite large, they are not true jointed legs (which are always attached to the thorax).

PRONOTUM. The upper surface of the prothorax.

PROTHORAX. The front-most of the three thoracic divisions (see THORAX).

PUPA (pl. *Pupae*). The life-history stage immediately preceding the adult stage in endopterygote (see above) insects. It is during this stage that the insects undergo the metamorphosis from larva into adult. Usually, the pupa is inactive but in some groups it may be temporarily active.

ROSTRUM. A beak-like extension to the head and/or mouthparts, found mainly in bugs (Order Hemiptera) and weevils (Order Coleoptera).

SCALE. A modified hair, forming a flattened plate-like structure. The differently coloured scales may give a striking coloration in butterflies and some moths. Also found in other animals, e.g. silverfish (Order Thysanura).

SECONDARY SEGMENTATION. See SEGMENT below.

SEGMENT. A section of the body of invertebrates, either of the main body or of the appendages (legs, palps, etc.). The segments are sometimes divided by visible joints, but in many invertebrates the underlying body segmentation may be hidden. Conversely, some animals may have "secondary" segments. These appear as true segments, with clear joints in between, but are in fact artefacts of surface ornamentation and do not reflect any "real" underlying body segmentation.

STIGMA. A dark spot on the forewings of insects, usually approximately half-way along the leading edge or close to the distal tip of the wing.

TARSUS. One of the major divisions of the arthropod leg. The outermost (distal) segment, which may itself be sub-divided into smaller segments (up to a maximum of five) (see Figure 1).

TARSAL SEGMENTS. The sub-segments which form the tarsus; up to five in number (see TARSUS, and Figure 1).

TIBIA (pl. *Tibiae*). One of the major divisions of the arthropod leg. In insects, it is the penultimate (second from last) segment—see Figure 1.

THORAX. One of the major body divisions in the arthropods. In the insects it is the middle of three divisions, lying behind the head and in front of the abdomen. The major locomotory appendages arise from it, i.e. the legs and wings. In other arthropods the thorax may be fused with the head, to form the cephalothorax. In insects, the thorax is itself divided into three sub-divisions—the pro-, meso- and metathorax.

VENTRAL. The lower side.

VESTIGIAL. Not fully developed.

ANTENNAE

When present, the antennae can take many forms - a selection of those which may be found are illustrated below

LEGS
Insect legs consist of five major sub-divisions: the coxa, trochanter, femur, tibia and tarsus. The tarsus may itself be divided into 2, 3, 4 or 5 segments, and may have 1 or 2 claws.

Coxa
Trochanter
Femur
Tibia
Tarsus

NUMBER OF WINGS

Wings may be absent from many insects. When present, wings will occur in one or two pairs. In those with a single pair, the "missing" pair may be modified into drumstick-shaped balancers (halteres)

Haltere

Abdomen

Thorax

Head

WINGS

Wings may be rudimentary, or incompletely developed. In four-winged forms, the front pair may be completely, or partially, hardened to form wing cases - see NOTE B, p. 703

Stigma

Open cell

Closed cell

Sucking

Biting

"Jaw"   Palp

MOUTHPARTS

Typically, mouthparts are either of the biting or sucking type.

Palps may be present, or absent. In some groups all mouthparts are greatly reduced, and may be missing completely.

Wing venation. Most membranous wings will have some form of venation (but not always). This may be complex, with "closed" cells being present. These are areas in the main body of the wing which are completely surrounded by veins. "Open" cells are those cells which border on the wing margin.

Some wings may have a pigmented area on the landing edge; this is referred to as the stigma in this key.

FIGURE 1. External features of a "typical" insect.

NOTES

KEY A
INTRODUCTORY KEY

A1   "True" jointed legs present . . .   A2
(see NOTE A opposite)

—   No "true" jointed legs . . . . **KEY B**
(page 704)
(see NOTE A opposite)

A2   Three pairs of *jointed* legs A3

Note: If your animal apparently has two pairs of legs, go to A3.

—   More than three pairs of true *jointed* legs
(see NOTE A opposite) . . . **KEY C**
(page 710)

A3   Wings present A4
(see NOTE B opposite)

—   Wings absent . . . . **KEY D**
(page 716)
(see NOTE B opposite)

A4   One pair of wings . . . . . **KEY E**
(page 734)

Note. In many insects having one pair of wings the second pair are reduced to two small drumstick-shaped appendages—the *halteres* (a). If halteres are present assume that your animal has one pair of wings and go to KEY E.

a

—   Two pairs of wings . . . . . **KEY F**
(page 736)

Note. Include all animals which have hardened or leathery upper wing cases, or incompletely developed wing pads (see NOTE B opposite), as having two pairs of wings.

NOTE A LEGS

Look carefully. The most likely source of confusion here will be with maggot- or caterpillar-like larvae. If jointed legs are present in these animals there will always be three pairs (a), and these will be situated immediately behind the head. Fleshy stumps—*prolegs* or "*claspers*"—may also appear further down the body but these are not true jointed legs (b).

NOTE B WINGS

Wings can be difficult to see and one mistake in particular is commonly made. In some insects the first pair are modified into hardened or leathery wing cases which protect the second pair of wings. These cases—the *elytra*—may be deeply pigmented and difficult to distinguish from the rest of the body. If in doubt, try teasing the suspected elytra apart and this will usually show whether or not they are really wing cases (a & b). The wing cases have become fused in some groups and will not be moved. Look for the "join" down the back (c); if this is present assume that the animal has two pairs of wings. In other groups the elytra may be very short (d), whilst in immature (nymphal) stages the wings may be incompletely developed and are easily overlooked (e & f). If short elytra or immature wing pads are present count the specimen as having two pairs of wings.

Don't worry, where there is doubt the animals will key out both ways.

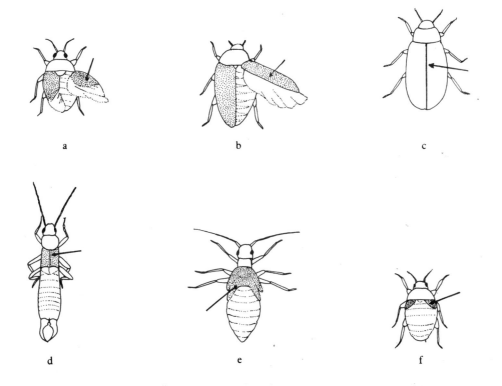

KEY B

ANIMALS WITH NO TRUE JOINTED LEGS. NO WINGS

B1   Shell present (snails and some slugs)   B2

—   No shell **B3**

B2   *This couplet will only work with living or recently dead animals*

—   Body, when withdrawn into the shell, is protected by a hard and horny cover—the *operculum* . . . . . **"Gilled" snails PROSOBRANCHIA** (p. 761)

—   The body, when withdrawn into the shell, is not protected by an operculum or the body cannot be fully withdrawn into the shell . . . **"Lunged" slugs and snails PULMONATA** (p. 761)

Note. Living snails may seal their shells with a thin film when resting during the day. This seal may be thicker and more opaque during times of drought, or when the snail is hibernating during the winter. Don't confuse this temporary seal—the *epiphragm*—with the *operculum* which is a permanent feature. If in doubt, prod the covering with a pencil; an epiphragm will break, an operculum won't.

B3   Body not obviously segmented. With or without head tentacles **B4**

—   Body obviously segmented—never with head tentacles. (Do not confuse segmented antennae with non-segmented tentacles.) **B7**

B4   Two sets of head tentacles. The upper pair
      are longer than the lower and may appear
      clubbed, sometimes with dark "eye" spots
      at their tips (a). Lower body with a "foot"
      fringe (b) . . . . **Slugs**
      PULMONATA
      (p. 761)

—   No such head tentacles, or if "horns" are
      present, then there is no flattened "foot"
      fringe **B5**

B5   Body is long and thin—many times longer
      than broad. Not flattened in cross-section
      (a). Never moves by "gliding" over the
      substrate, and cannot alter the body width
      during movement . . . .
      Hairworms and Eelworms
      NEMATODA & NEMATOMORPHA
      (difficult to separate, see notes on p. 746)

—   Body flattened in cross-section (b,c), in
      part at least (if in doubt look at the lower
      part of the body—the *sole*). Animal moves
      by "gliding" over the substrate, and when
      active it can contract and extend its body
      to several times its "normal" resting
      length **B6**

B6 Eyes arranged in two groups, with 3 or 8 eyes in each (a); never with two large eyes only. Can extend the proboscis from the head when alive (b). Two longitudinal darker stripes pass down the whole length of the body. . . . . . **ribbon worm NEMERTEA**
(p. 747)

— Eyes not arranged in two groups of 3 or 8 eyes; either numerous eyes scattered over front end, or two single eyes (c). No proboscis (the mouth opens on the ventral surface). No longitudinal stripes, or if present, these merge or fade well short of the head end (d) . . . . . **free-living flatworms TURBELLARIA**
(p. 747)

Note. Care should be taken here. Only one British species of ribbon worm, *Argonemertes dendyi*, has been recorded and is thought to be very rare. Make sure that you haven't got the similar flatworm, *Microplana terrestris*, which has no proboscis.

B7 Less than 20 body segments . . . **B8**

— More than 20 body segments. . . **B15**

B8 Has a distinct head capsule, although this may be partly retracted into the body behind (if in doubt, look for antennae and external mouthparts. One, or both, of these structures will be present in animals with a head capsule) **B9**

— No head capsule apparent. . . . **B14**

B9 The body segment immediately behind the head is much larger than the two following it, its length being equal to, or longer than, their combined length (a,b) .
**larvae of
wood and bark boring beetles
COLEOPTERA**
(p. 760)

— The three segments behind the head are approximately equal in size, or if one of the three segments behind the head is larger than the other two, it is *not* the one immediately behind the head (c) . B10

B10 The body is not covered in long bristles or spines B11

— The body is covered by long bristles or spines—some being as long as, or longer than, the width of the abdominal segments B12

B11 The long axis of the head (in side profile) points downwards (or slightly forwards) with mouthparts also pointing downwards or slightly forwards so that they are not visible when viewed from above the head (a). . . **Weevil (beetle) larvae
COLEOPTERA**
(p. 760)

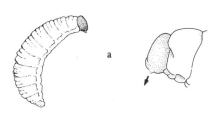

— The long axis of the head and the mouthparts points forwards (b). The mouthparts can be seen from above. . . . . . .
**Two-winged fly larvae
DIPTERA**
(p. 759)

Note: These two groups can be very difficult to distinguish; if in doubt consult a specialist textbook (see the notes on p. 759–760). Weevil larvae are vegetarian, and will most often be found in rolled leaves, amongst roots, or tunnelling under bark, in stems or in nuts. Diptera larvae may be carnivorous or omnivorous and will be found almost anywhere.

B12 Animals associated with a nest or refuge belonging to a mammal or a bird . B13

— Animal not associated with a nest or refuge . . . **Two-winged fly larvae DIPTERA** (p. 759)

B13 Pale and worm-like. Long bristles in single bands encircling each segment. Prominent one-segmented antenna. Thirteen body segments (not including the head); all "simple", lacking any surface structure (prolegs, suction pads, etc.) except the last (anal) segment which has a pair of tube-like extensions **Flea larvae SIPHONAPTERA** (p. 759)

— Without this combination of characters . **Two-winged fly larvae DIPTERA** (p. 759)

B14 Darker pigmented "skeletal" structures can be seen inside the head end. The animal may have lobes, bristles or tail-like extensions on its body, but not always (see Figure 2, p. 709) **Two-winged fly larvae DIPTERA** (p. 759)

Note: Although these structures, internal mouthparts, are usually highlighted against the pale flesh they are easier to see if the animal is gently squeezed between two microscope slides.

— No darker internal structures visible in the head, even when squeezing the animal. Never with long lobes, bristles or tail-like extensions .   . **Bee, ant or wasp larvae HYMENOPTERA (Apocrita)** (p. 760)

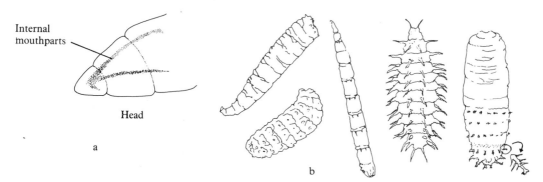

Internal mouthparts

Head

a

b

FIGURE 2. Diptera larvae. (a) Close-up of a head, (b) a range of whole larvae (From Skidmore, 1985).

B15 Suckers present, usually at both ends of the body. No clitellum . . . **Leeches HIRUDINEA** (p. 748)

— No suckers present on the body. There may be a band, formed by fused segments, part-way along the body (the *clitellum*) B16

B16 More than 30 body segments. There may be a band, formed by fused segments, part-way along the body (the *clitellum*) .

Earthworms and Whiteworms OLIGOCHAETA (p. 748)

— Less than 30 body segments. No clitellum. See Figure 2 also. . . . .

Two-winged fly larvae DIPTERA (p. 759)

Note. Dipterous larvae which appear to have more than 15 body segments are displaying "secondary" segmentation—see the glossary. Also, if you look closely you will probably see a head capsule which has been overlooked previously.

KEY C

ANIMALS WITH MORE THAN THREE PAIRS OF JOINTED LEGS. NO WINGS

C1 More than four pairs of jointed legs. Antennae present or absent . . . **C2**

— Four pairs of jointed legs. No antennae
. . . . **C16**

C2 Two pairs of antennae obviously present, clearly separated at the base. The body is flattened side-to-side to give a shrimp-like appearance **Sand hoppers or "Scuds"
AMPHIPODA**
(p. 751)

Note: Another group of crustaceans, the copepods, may be found in leaf litter. Always smaller than 1 mm, these will have two pairs of antennae of which the upper is the larger; in the sand hoppers (above) the lower is the largest (see notes on p. 751).

— Only a single pair of antennae clearly present, or antennae absent . . . **C3**

C3 Antennae clearly branched, with branches originating some way from the base (a). Less than 2 mm long . **PAUROPODA**
(p. 751)

— Antennae unbranched, or absent. Often larger than 2 mm. **C4**

C4 Body relatively broad in dorsal view; length never more than three times the width. The living animal may roll into an almost spherical ball when disturbed **C5**

— Body relatively narrow in dorsal view; length greater than three times the width. Although the living animal may curl up, it never rolls into a tight ball . . . **C6**

C5   6 or 7 pairs of walking legs. Looking from above, the hind end of the body terminates in a series of short abdominal segments, usually with projections (uropods) . . . **Woodlice ISOPODA** (p. 750)

Note. The woodlice are crustaceans (see p. 750), and, consequently, have two pairs of antennae. However, one pair is minute and easily overlooked and has been ignored in this key, to help ease-of-use.

—   Up to 17 pairs of legs. Body never terminates in a series of narrow abdominal segments. (Beware! See the note on pillbugs below) . . . . . . **Pill millipedes GLOMERIDA** (p. 751)

Note. The pillbug woodlice, *Armadillidium* spp., may easily be confused with the pill millipedes. Both can roll into a ball. The pillbug woodlice have narrow terminal abdominal segments (see Fig. a), whereas these are absent in the millipedes (Fig. b). Another millipede—*Polyxenus lagurus*—may key out here. This species is covered in a series of hair tufts, unlike the pill millipedes which are smooth (see C10).

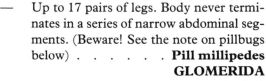

a   b

C6   One pair of legs per body segment. Antennae long—over 14 segments (in adults) C7

Note. Make sure that you are looking at the right end! Some centipedes have terminal abdominal appendages which look like antennae but have less than 6 segments.

—   Two pairs of legs per body segment. Antennae relatively short—never more than 8 segments Millipedes DIPLOPODA . . . C10

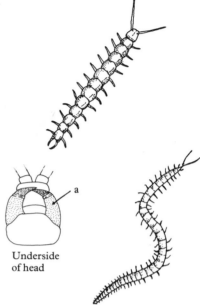

C7   Less than 15 mm long. Never more than
     12 pairs of legs. Front legs not modified
     into a set of claws   .   .   **SYMPHYLA**
                                        (p. 752)

Note. Very rarely, recently hatched immature centipedes may key out here. These will have a pair of
claws (the forcipules), but may have as few as four
pairs of legs; the others are added as the juvenile
undergoes a series of moults.

—   Up to 75 mm long. Often with many more
     than 12 pairs of legs. Front legs modified
     into a pair of claws (forcipules (a))
     CHILOPODA Centipedes   .   .   .   C8

Underside
of head

C8   7 to 15 pairs of legs . . . .
                Surface-dwelling centipedes
                LITHOBIOMORPHA
                                        (p. 752)

—   More than 20 pairs of legs C9

C9   21 pairs of legs (may lose the last pair of
     legs if mishandled). Fast moving   .   .   .
                Surface-dwelling centipedes
                SCOLOPENDROMORPHA
                                        (p. 752)

—   31 to 80 pairs of legs. Slow moving .   .   .
                Soil-living centipedes
                GEOPHILOMORPHA
                                        (p. 752)

C10 Surface of each body segment bearing two transverse rows of spines, with two clumps of bristles **"Bristly" Millipedes POLYXENIDA** (p. 751)

— Without the arrangement of spines and bristles described above C11

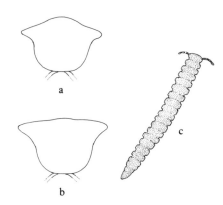

C11 With keel-like extensions to the side of each body segment, giving the upper part of each segment a flattened appearance in cross-section (a & b). When viewed from above, the outline of the body is deeply serrated (c). C12

— Without keel-like extensions on the sides of the body segments. Often approximately circular in cross section (d), but if flattened, then there are no keels (e) and the body outline is not deeply serrated in profile (when viewed from above) (f,g) C13

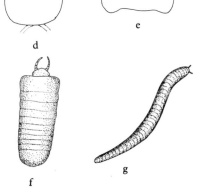

C12 Adults with a maximum of 20 body segments . . . **Flat-backed Millipedes POLYDESMIDA** (p. 751)

— Adults with up to 30 body segments . . **Millipedes CHORDEUMATIDA (sub-order Craspedosomatidea)** (p. 751)

C13 The upper surface of each body segment forms a roof-like dome. The millipede appears flattened in cross-section (a,b), with body width (not including legs) more than 1.5 times the body depth (not including legs) C14

— The upper surface of each body segment does not form a roof-like dome. Often approximately circular in cross-section (c); body width roughly equal to body depth, never exceeding the ratio of 1.5 : 1 . . . . C15

C14 Body segments, 12 or fewer. The living animal can roll into a spherical ball. Widespread throughout the British Isles. . . **Pill Millipedes GLOMERIDA** (p. 751)

— More than 12 body segments. The living animal can roll up, but not into a spherical ball. Restricted to Southeast England . . **Millipedes POLYZONIIDA** (p. 751)

C15 *Count the number of pairs of legs along one side of the millipede (1,2,3 . . . . etc.)*

— The total number of pairs of legs is an odd number. . . . **"Snake" Millipedes JULIDA** (p. 751)

— The total number of pairs of legs is an even number. . . . . . . **Millipedes CHORDEUMATIDA (sub-order Chordeumatidea)** (p. 751)

C16 Large pincer-like palps present . . C17

— No such palps C18

Note. Do not confuse pincer palps (a) with the very long palps in some spiders. The tips of the latter will not be clawed, but will look more like boxing gloves (b).

C17 Abdomen ends in a long tapering "tail" (the *telson*) (a). Body (not including claws) more than 20 mm long . . . **Scorpions SCORPIONIDA** (p. 749)

— Abdomen ends abruptly, not in a long tail (b). Body (not including claws) less than 5 mm long . . . . **"False" scorpions PSEUDOSCORPIONIDA** (p. 749)

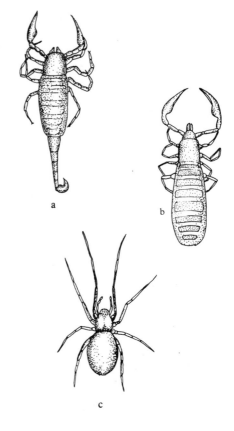

a   b

C18 Thorax and abdomen separated by a constricted "waist"—the *pedicel* (c) . . . **Spiders ARANEAE** (p. 749)

— Thorax and abdomen fused into one— look from above C19

c

C19 Body clearly segmented—if in doubt look from below. Legs usually more than 1.5 times the length of the body. Body (not including legs) usually larger than 2 mm . **Harvestmen OPILIONES** (p. 749)

a

Note. Segmentation may be difficult to observe in very small individuals. In these cases harvestmen will always have a wart-like projection on the front half of the upper surface (the eye-bearing *ocularium*) (a) which is never present in mites or ticks.

— Body apparently not segmented. Legs rarely longer than the body and usually much shorter. Body only larger than 2 mm in a small minority of species. . . . . **Mites & Ticks ACARI** (p. 750)

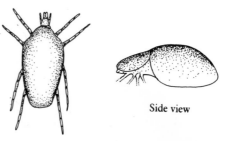

Side view

Top view

KEY D

ANIMALS WITH THREE PAIRS OF JOINTED LEGS. NO WINGS

D1   Animal lives in a tubular *transportable* case (which it carries around with it) constructed of silk, sand grains, hairs, plant material, etc D2

> **Note.** Beware! Larvae of several groups of insects protect or camouflage themselves with fragments of vegetation, sand, etc. But in most cases this covering does *not* form a tube. If you can see the under surface of the animal by turning it over without removing the covering, take the second lead, i.e. go to D4.

—   Animal not living in a tubular *transportable* case as above, although it may have a tubular refuge which is fixed to the substrate or vegetation D4

D2   *Unfortunately the three groups keying out in D2 and D3 cannot be distinguished on ecological characters alone. You will need to remove the animal, but if you agitate the case or heat it gently in sunshine the animal may emerge without any need to destroy the case*

—   Abdominal prolegs present (a) . . . . .
The "Bagworms"
(larvae of the family Psychidae)
LEPIDOPTERA
(p. 758)

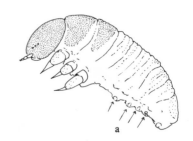

—   No abdominal prolegs present . . D3

D3 A pair of anal claws present on the rear tip of the abdomen; also, a fleshy lump on the dorsal surface of the 1st abdominal segment. Very bristly—some head bristles longer than legs. Mainly in deciduous leaf litter in the Wyre Forest area. . . . .
**Cased caddis larvae
TRICHOPTERA**
(p. 758)

— No anal claws or dorsal fleshy lump on the abdomen. Not particularly bristly—never with bristles as long as legs. Mainly found in coniferous woods, often associated with ants' nests . . . **Cased beetle larvae
COLEOPTERA**
(p. 760)

D4 "Caterpillar-like". The body is soft and fleshy—often with stumpy abdominal "prolegs", in addition to the true jointed legs **D5**

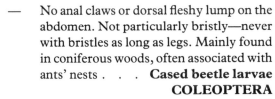

Note. This couplet is included to save time. Don't worry if you are uncertain; "difficult" groups will key out both ways.

— Not particularly "caterpillar-like" . **D10**

D5 Nine or fewer (where some are fused) segments behind the head. The four-segmented antennae are clearly visible from above . . . . . **Springtails
COLLEMBOLA**
(p. 753)

Note. Recently hatched millipede larvae may be mistaken occasionally for soil-dwelling springtails. These will never be larger than 1.5 mm, usually 0.5 mm or less. They will often have relatively long legs which appear 5–6 segmented, nearly as long as the depth of the abdomen (a). Springtails' legs appear 3–4 segmented and are shorter (b). Millipedes' heads may appear circular or semi-oval in side profile but in springtails the heads are more flattened.

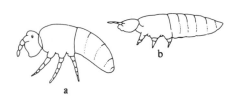

— More than nine segments behind the head. Antennae comparatively inconspicuous from above, or apparently missing . **D6**

D6　No abdominal prolegs (see p. 703) .　D7

—　Prolegs present on the abdomen (see p. 703) D8

D7　Head oval in side view, with long axis pointing downwards or slightly forwards. Antennae inconspicuous, or apparently absent. Body never covered in hairs. Various colours, but never black throughout. Often found in groups of five or more, sometimes in a "web" of silky threads. .

Sawfly larvae
HYMENOPTERA
(Sub-order Symphyta)
(p. 760)

—　Head flattened in side view, with the long axis pointing forwards. Antennae often obviously present, originating from the front corners of the head (when viewed from above). Various colours, but sometimes black throughout. Usually found individually, rarely in twos and threes, and never in a "web" of silky threads.

Beetle larvae
and, rarely, wingless adults
see D19 note if in doubt
COLEOPTERA
(p. 760)

Note. Very rarely, snow flea larvae (Mecoptera—*Boreus hyemalis*) may key out here. These are found in short moss in sandy areas, are less than 3 mm long, and are usually pale yellowish and have a clearly curved body shape.

D8　4, or fewer, pairs of abdominal prolegs (not including the claspers on the last abdominal segment) . . . .

Larvae of Butterflies and Moths
LEPIDOPTERA
(p. 758)

—　5 or more pairs of prolegs (not including those on the last abdominal segment)　D9

D9   8 pairs of prolegs (not including those on
     the last abdominal segments).   .   .   .
                        Scorpion fly larvae
                            MECOPTERA
                                (p. 758)

—   5, 6 or 7 pairs of prolegs (not including
     those on the last abdominal segment).
     Often with a distinctive black spot on their
     head capsule .   .   .   .   **Sawfly larvae**
                        (Sub-order Symphyta)
                            HYMENOPTERA
                                (p. 760)

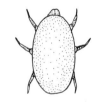

Note. Some moth larvae may key out here. These
will be very small, less than 5 mm, and associated
with moss. They are also distinguished by having
hooks on the ends of their prolegs, which are never
present in sawfly or scorpion fly larvae.

D10 Antennae not present (or strongly reduced
     and thus apparently absent) .   .   . D11

—   Antennae present D16

D11 Abdomen not segmented, and apparently
     fused to the thorax. Body length less than
     1 mm .   .   .   . **Mite larvae**
                                    ACARI
                                (p. 750)

—   Abdomen segmented. Body length often
     larger than 1 mm, usually much larger
     .   .   .   . D12

D12 Legs not easily seen; often hidden under
     the body. Clings to plant surface   .   .   .
                        Female Scale Insects
                HEMIPTERA (Family Coccoidea)
                                (p. 756)

Note. Scale insects are a difficult group to identify.
The insect is covered in a waxy scale which has to be
lifted off before the animal can be seen. They also
lack clear external features and have a wide variety of
shapes, some of which are illustrated in Figure 3
overleaf.

—   Legs easily seen. Animal can be fully
     mobile, not clinging to plant surface D13

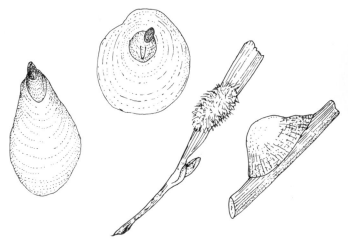

FIGURE 3. A range of scale insects—actual animals up to 3 mm long. (After Green, 1922).

D13 Body laterally compressed—flattened from side-to-side. Never more than 9 mm 'ong . . . . **Fleas SIPHONAPTERA** (p. 759)

— Body not laterally compressed . . D14

D14 Free living. Abdomen elongate, length more than twice the width (look from above). Not particularly flattened from top-to-bottom (dorso-ventrally) . D15

— External parasites, mainly on vertebrates but may be found off their host. Abdomen short, its length rarely more than twice the width (look from above), and often flattened from top-to-bottom (dorso-ventrally) D52

D15 Head pointed in front to give the animal a characteristic "torpedo" shape. Front legs held forward, like a pair of "feelers". Body length less than 2 mm . . **PROTURA** (p. 753)

— Head not tapering in front to give torpedo shape. Usually larger than 2 mm . . . **Beetle larvae** **COLEOPTERA** (p. 760)

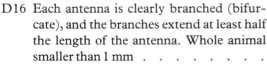

D16 Each antenna is clearly branched (bifurcate), and the branches extend at least half the length of the antenna. Whole animal smaller than 1 mm . . . . **larval PAUROPODA** (p. 751)

— Antennae unbranched, or only slightly branched (i.e. near the tip of the antennae). Whole animal usually larger than 1 mm, but not always D17

Head side view

D17 Mouthparts formed into a segmented sucking tube which is held under the body, pointing downwards or backwards. Mouthparts without segmented palps . . **Bugs** **HEMIPTERA** (p. 756)

Note. Very rarely, Anoplura (sucking lice), wingless Diptera and Lepidoptera could cause problems here. The lice are easily distinguished by their short and stout legs (shorter than the width of the abdomen), with a single tarsal segment terminating in a single large claw. Diptera and Lepidoptera will have five (or apparently four) tarsal segments (Hemiptera have a maximum of three), and may have segmented palpal mouthparts also.

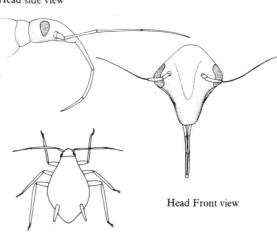

Head Front view

Top view

— Mouthparts don't form a tube which is held under the body. If uncertain look for segmented palps; if these are present choose this lead D18

D18   The pronotum (the upper part of the first thoracic segment) extends over the head to form a shield-like covering when the animal is viewed from above . . .   D19

—   Most of the dorsal surface of the head visible D20

D19   Antennae very long—nearly as long as, or longer than, the body. Many more than 11 antennal segments (a) . . **Cockroaches DICTYOPTERA** (p. 755)

—   Antennae relatively short—never longer than the width of the pronotum. Up to 11 antennal segments (b) . . **Beetle larvae (and, rarely, wingless adults) COLEOPTERA** (p. 760)

Note. Adult beetles will have 5 tarsal segments on each leg, and 11 antennal segments. Larvae will not have this combination.

D20   Hind legs are strongly adapted for jumping (a). Hind femurs are at least twice as wide and long as those on the front pairs of legs. Pronotum (the upper part of the first thoracic segment) is usually shaped as shown (b) (though it will be less apparent in young nymphs, and much longer in ground hoppers). . . . .
Grasshoppers, ground hoppers and crickets ORTHOPTERA (p. 755)

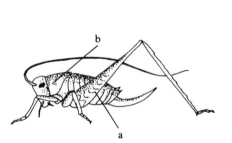

—   Without this combination of leg and pronotum features D21

D21 2 or 3 "tails" or projecting appendages (cerci) on terminal segments of the abdomen D22

  Note. Beware of broken tails. Most animals are symmetrical; if a tail on one side is not complemented by a similar appendage on the other look for a remnant—a stub, a broken base, etc.

— Terminal "tails" absent or very short, or only one (though this may divide towards the tip) D32

D22 3 abdominal appendages present . D23

— 2 abdominal appendages present . D24

  Note. Beware of breakages.

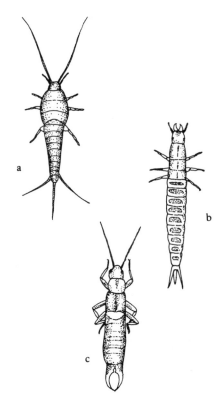

D23 Antennae long, at least 1.5 times the width of the head (a). Body carrot-shaped; becoming narrower from front to back .

  Three-pronged bristletails THYSANURA (p. 753)

a

— Antennae short, less than 1.5 times the width of the head (b). Body rarely carrot-shaped . . . . . **Beetle larvae COLEOPTERA** (p. 760)

b

D24 Abdominal appendages are strong and curved inwards (c) . . . . **Earwigs DERMAPTERA** (p. 754)

— Abdominal appendages not as broad, and not curved, or only slightly so . . D25

c

D25 Abdominal appendages are long and thin, at least one quarter the length of the abdomen D26

— Appendages are shorter than one quarter the length of the abdomen . . . D29

D26 Look from above. Abdominal appendages converge, or are parallel, or diverge only slightly so that the distance between the tips is never greater than the width of the abdomen (a) D27

Note. In marginal cases—if the appendages have bristles longer than the diameter of the "tail", choose the second lead, i.e. go to D28. If they don't have bristles, or have bristles which are narrower than the width of the tail, choose the first lead; i.e. go to D27

— Abdominal appendages diverge from their base so that the distance between their tips is greater than the width of the abdomen when viewed from above (b) . . . D28

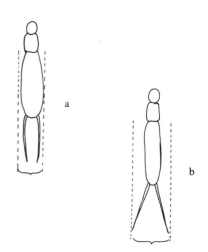

Side views

D27 Nine or fewer body segments behind the head. Antennae four- or six-segmented. Abdominal appendages are joined at, or near, the base. Often with a wart-like tube under the abdomen, between, or just behind, the hind legs . . **Springtails COLLEMBOLA** (p. 753)

Note. Rarely, "secondary" segmentation of the antennae may cause problems. In these cases the antennae have surface grooves which may look like the joins between true segments and could give the impression that there are more than the "true" number of segments. However, the number of body segments, the "tail" and the wart-like tube will be sufficient for identification.

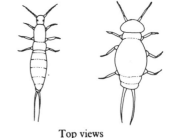

Top views

— More than nine body segments behind the head. Eight or more antennal segments. Abdominal appendages are clearly separate at their bases and originate from the outward hind corners of the abdomen. Never with a wart-like tube under the body. . . . . . **Earwig nymphs DERMAPTERA** (p. 754)

D28 Long antennae—at least 2.5 times as long as the width of the head (a). Animal less than 5 mm long. "Tails" are composed of many segments . . . .
Two-pronged bristle tails
DIPLURA
(p. 753)

Note. Occasionally, springtails (Collembola) and some adult stoneflies (Plecoptera) with vestigial wings may key out here. In the springtails, the antennae never have more than four segments and the body behind the head is clearly nine-segmented. The stoneflies are usually found near running water, are dark-coloured, have compound eyes and three tarsal segments per leg. In contrast, bristletails are widespread, are pale coloured, have no compound eyes and only one tarsal segment per leg.

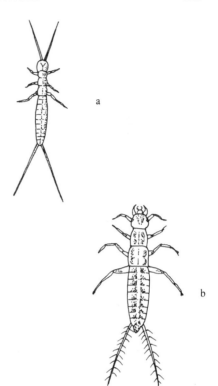

— Antennae are never longer than twice the width of the head (b). Often larger than 5 mm. "Tails" unsegmented, or consisting of less than 5 segments. . . . . .
Beetle larvae
COLEOPTERA
(p. 760)

D29 Abdominal appendages are short, located forward of the tip of the abdomen and above the lateral mid-line D30

— Not as above D31

D30 Mouthparts forming a sucking tube (look under the head, and also between the bases of the front legs). No segmented palps
Bugs
HEMIPTERA
(p. 756)

Head
Side view

Head
Front view

— Biting mouthparts, or no obvious tube-like structure. Segmented palps present
Beetle larvae
COLEOPTERA
(p. 760)

Segmented palps

Head top view

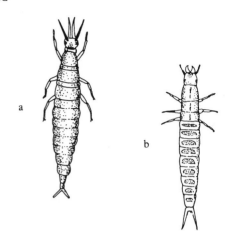

Top view

D31 Antennae approximately twice as long as the width of the head; long, piercing mouthparts (a) . . **Lacewing larvae NEUROPTERA** (p. 757)

— Antennae usually shorter than 2 times the width of the head; biting mouthparts (b) . . . . .Beetle larvae **COLEOPTERA** (p. 760)

Side view

D32 The body is sharply constricted into a waist between the abdomen and the thorax (look carefully; if you are unsure look from the side as well as from above) . . . . **apterous (wingless) Bees, Ants and Wasps (Sub-Order Apocrita) HYMENOPTERA** (p. 760)

Note. Booklice (Psocoptera) may key out here. These *always* have two- or three-segmented tarsi and are rarely longer than 3 mm. (Hymenoptera nearly always have 5)

— No sharply constricted "waist" between the abdomen and thorax D33

D33 Ten, or more, antennal segments . D34

— Less than ten antennal segments . D42

Note. The antennal segmentation may be difficult to see in smaller specimens. These specimens should key out both ways, but check nevertheless by keying through both sections. Also, beware of breakages. If one antenna is obviously longer than the other count the number of segments on the former. If in doubt, key both ways and you will probably find that you arrive at the same answer anyway.

D34 Body is clothed in a dense covering of scales (which may appear as hairs) . . .
Wingless female Moths
LEPIDOPTERA
(p. 758)

— Body not densely clothed in scales or hairs
. . . . D35

D35 Body is unusually long and thin, at least eight times longer than broad . . . .
Stick insects
PHASMIDA
(p. 754)

— Body not particularly long and thin   D36

D36 Head is extended downwards, forming an obvious "beak" . . . . **Snow fleas**
MECOPTERA
(p. 758)

— Head not forming a "beak" . . . D37

D37 Long antennae (beware of broken antennae), their length at least 2 times the width of the head. D38

— Antennae no more than 1.5 times as long as the width of the head D40

D38 Rudimentary wings present on the side of the thorax (look closely). Body larger than 7 mm . . . .
"wingless" adult female Caddis flies
TRICHOPTERA
(p. 758)

— No rudimentary wings on the side of the thorax. Body, often (but *not* always) smaller than 5 mm D39

D39 The main body (thorax and abdomen) has a fusiform (i.e. tapered at both ends) or oval shape (look from above). Large piercing jaws (a), or club-shaped mouthparts (b), project in front of the head. Sometimes larger than 5 mm. . . . . . .

Lacewing larvae
NEUROPTERA
(p. 757)

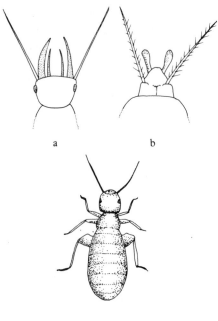

— At least partly "waisted" between thorax and abdomen, thus not forming a fusiform or oval shape. Never have large piercing jaws, or club-shaped mouthparts, projecting in front of the head. Always less than 5 mm long . . . . **Booklice**
PSOCOPTERA
(p. 756)

D40 Tarsi of the legs are five-segmented. Antennae 11-segmented. Jaws are not visible from above (a,b) . . . . . .

wingless adult Beetles
COLEOPTERA
(p. 760)

Note. Sometimes, "winged" beetles may key out here, in which case you have missed the short wing cases (c)—see NOTE B, p. 703.

— Either the tarsi are not five-segmented, or the antennae have less than 11 segments. Jaws are visible from above (d,e) . D41

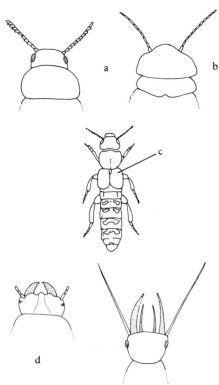

D41 Antennae thread-like (with the segmentation difficult to see), at least as long as the
width of the head, but often much longer.
Jaws long and projecting well in front of
the head (look from above) (a). Body
usually broadest towards the middle, and
tapering towards the ends (b) . . . .
Lacewing larvae
NEUROPTERA
(p. 757)

a   b

— Antennae stout, clearly segmented, and
often shorter than the width of the head.
Jaws strongly curved and usually folded
in front of the head so that they over-
lap (c). Abdomen often parallel-sided, or
broadest at the front end (d) . . . . .
Beetle larvae
COLEOPTERA
(p. 760)

c

d

D42 Legs indistinct, often hidden under the
body. Clings to plant surface. See Figure
3, p. 720 . . . **female Scale Insects**
HEMIPTERA
(p. 756)

Note. Scale insects are a difficult group to identify.
The insect is covered in a waxy scale which has to be
lifted off before the body can be seen. They often lack
clear external features and have a wide variety of
shapes, some of which are illustrated on p. 720.

— Legs easily seen. Animal is freely mobile,
and not firmly attached to the surface of a
plant D43

D43 Nine body segments behind the head, with a bilobed wart-like tube under the first abdominal segment (you may have to tease the hind set of legs apart to see this). Usually with a springing organ trailing behind the abdomen or tucked underneath . . . . **Springtails** **· COLLEMBOLA** (p. 753)

> **Note.** In some springtails (Collembola) the springing organ is missing, but the ventral tube is usually present. Minute, recently hatched millipede larvae may be mistaken for soil-dwelling springtails. See note under D5.

— More than nine body segments behind the head, with no springing organ . . D44

D44 Body laterally compressed—looks as if it has been squashed from side-to-side **Fleas** **SIPHONAPTERA** (p. 759)

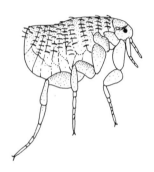

— Body is not obviously laterally compressed D45

D45 The upper surface of the head and the first segment of the thorax—the prothorax (a)—are hardened and shiny, and clearly very different from the other two thoracic segments (b). The prothorax is very elongated, at least 1.5 times as long as the next thoracic segment (the mesothorax) . . . **Snakefly larvae and pupae** **MEGALOPTERA** (p. 757)

— The prothorax is no more hardened or shiny than the following two thoracic segments; usually not obviously extended D46

D46 Strong jaws projecting in front of the head
(when viewed from above (a,b)—these
may appear as two individual stylets . .
D41

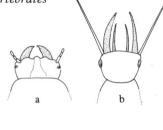

— Jaws do not clearly project in front of the
head, and where the mouthparts have
been adapted into a tube-like structure,
this is always held underneath the body,
pointing backwards. D47

a   b

D47 The head is narrow, less than one third of
the maximum body width (look from
above) . . . . **Sucking lice**
PHTHIRAPTERA
(Sub-Order Anoplura)
(p. 756)

— The head is not narrow, its width being
greater than one third of the maximum
body width (look from above)   . . D48

D48 Mouthparts forming a segmented rigid
tube, which is held under the body pointing downwards or backwards. Without
segmented palps . . . .
apterous (wingless)
adult and nymphal Bugs
HEMIPTERA
(p. 756)

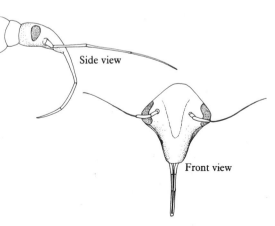

Side view

Front view

— Mouthparts not forming a tube, and often
with segmented palps D49

D49 Distinct antennae—as long as, or longer
than, the width of the head   . . . D50

— Antennae very inconspicuous—length
less than the width of the head . . D51

D50 More than nine antennal segments (although these may be difficult to see). Each antenna consists of two large basal segments followed by a flagellum of 11–20 or more segments. Head relatively large, its length at least 1/4 the length of the rest of the body. The body often appears pale and almost translucent with background lighting. . . . . **Booklice PSOCOPTERA** (p. 756)

— Nine, or fewer, antennal segments. Antennae never consisting of two larger basal segments followed by a flagellum. Head relatively small, its length rarely exceeding more than one quarter the length of the rest of the body. Body not translucent with background lighting . . **Thrips THYSANOPTERA** (p. 757)

Note. Very rarely, wingless adult Diptera may key out through both leads above. These will have five tarsal segments, whereas booklice and thrips will have a maximum of three.

D51 Various sizes, ofter larger than 6 mm. Where smaller than 6 mm abdomen widest in the front quarter of its length, either tapering towards the back end, or parallel-sided for most of its length and tapering in the last quarter. Free living . . . . . . **Beetle larvae COLEOPTERA** (p. 760)

— Smaller than 6 mm. Abdomen not as above. Either almost oval (from above), or widest towards the middle of its length and tapering towards each end. Often associated with birds and mammals (also, sometimes bees), either as external parasites, or through phoresis ("hitching a lift"). D52

D52 Obvious "neck" present between the head and the thorax. Tarsi one- or two-segmented. . . . . . **Biting lice PHTHIRAPTERA (Sub-Order Mallophaga)** (p. 756)

— No distinct neck present—the head often sunk into the thorax. Tarsi five-segmented. Mainly associated with birds and mammals (particularly bats), but also found on bees. . . . . **wingless adult (two-winged) Flies DIPTERA** (p. 759)

KEY E

ANIMALS WITH THREE PAIRS OF JOINTED LEGS. ONE PAIR OF WINGS

E1 Abdomen terminating in "tails", or clumps of bristles E2

— No appendages on the tip of the abdomen E4

E2 Two or three long "tails" present, and these are longer than the length of the abdomen (beware of breakages). Complex wing venation; many "closed" cells. Antennae shorter than the width of the head. . . . . **Mayflies EPHEMEROPTERA** (p. 753)

— Abdomen terminating in one (a), two (b) or four (c) tapering "tails", or a pair of appendages which may (d), or may not (e), be adorned with a clump of bristles, but are never longer than the abdomen. Simple wing venation, with or without "closed" cells. Antennae usually longer than the width of the head, although only occasionally it may be shorter . . .E3

E3 Abdomen terminating in one (a), two (b) or four (c) tapering "tails", or paired clumps of bristles (d). Simple wing venation; no closed cells and less than three veins reaching the outer wing margin. Body less than 1.5 mm long. One tarsal segment per leg

male "Scale" Insects HEMIPTERA (Family Coccoidea) (p. 756)

— Abdomen terminating with a narrow pair of appendages which do not end in two clumps of bristles. Five or more veins reaching the outer wing margin. Body often larger than 1.5 mm. Five tarsal segments per leg . . . .

two-winged Flies or "true" flies DIPTERA (p. 759)

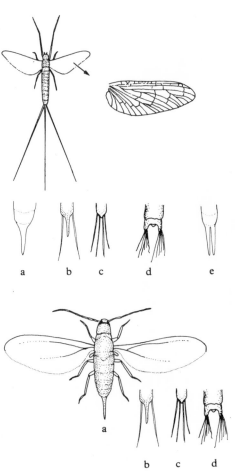

a   b   c   d   e

a

b   c   d

E4   Club-like balancers (halteres) in front of the wings. Wings as broad as, or broader than, long (a). Body less than 3 mm long. Distinctive antennae (b) . . . . . .
STREPSIPTERA
(p. 761)

a

b

—   Halteres located behind the wings (c,d). Wings are never as broad as long. Body often larger than 3 mm. Antennae usually simple (e) . . . .
**Two-winged, or "true", flies
DIPTERA**
(p. 759)

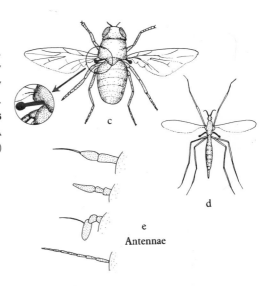

c

d

e
Antennae

Note. Halteres may sometimes be hidden by a membranous flap (f). Don't worry; in these cases the antennal characters will separate these two groups.

Top view
Membranous flap
f

IF YOUR SPECIMEN DOES NOT KEY OUT HERE GO TO **KEY F.** YOU HAVE MISSED A PAIR OF WINGS, OR YOUR SPECIMEN'S HIND WINGS HAVEN'T DEVELOPED YET.

KEY F

ANIMALS WITH THREE PAIRS OF JOINTED LEGS. TWO PAIRS OF WINGS

F1   Animal covered in a white powdery dust
or wax F2

Note. Do not confuse pale hairs with dust or wax, if in doubt, go to F3.

—   Animal not covered in white dust or wax
. . . . F3

F2   Wings held roof-like over the body.
Simple venation in the forewings, with
less than four veins reaching the wing
margin (although these may not be very
obvious) . . . . **Whiteflies
HEMIPTERA**
(p. 756)

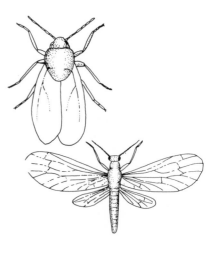

—   Wings not held roof-like over body. Wing
venation quite complex, with at least eight
veins reaching the margin of the forewings
**NEUROPTERA
(Family Coniopterygidae)**
(p. 757)

F3   The front wings form hardened or
leathery covers (the *elytra*; see NOTE
B, p. 703) under which the fully membranous hind wings are usually withdrawn
and hidden. Venation is missing completely from the elytra (though there may
be a surface pattern: ridges, grooves, pits,
etc.). Remember, the elytra may be very
short and extend only part-way down the
abdomen F4

—   Front wings do not form elytra. Both sets
of wings are completely or partly membranous, with varying amounts of venation
(but the veins may be covered in scales or
hairs); or both sets of wings may appear as
strap-like pads F7

F4   Two long, strongly curved (pincer-like) abdominal tails (cerci) . . . **Earwigs DERMAPTERA** (p. 754)

—   No pincer-like cerci. F5

F5   Antennae apparently absent or, if present, consisting of twelve or less antennal segments (look carefully—some antennae may appear long but only have three or four segments). The antennae are *usually* "simple" or "threadlike" (a), but *sometimes* may have an obvious "club" at the end (b) F6

—   Antennae consisting of more than twelve segments; *never* with a large "club" (ie. never as illustrated in b) F14

Note. Antennal segmentation can be difficult to see. Don't worry, awkward groups should key out both ways but check anyway if in doubt. Also, beware of breakages; if one antenna is longer than the other count the segmentation of the longer one.

F6   Mouthparts forming a segmented tube
     (a,b). This may be short, in which case the
     "beak" gives the head profile a character-
     istic triangular shape when viewed from in
     front (c). The beak may be carried curved
     backwards (reflexed) under the body.
     Mouthparts lack segmented palps . . .

     Bugs
     HEMIPTERA
     (p. 756)

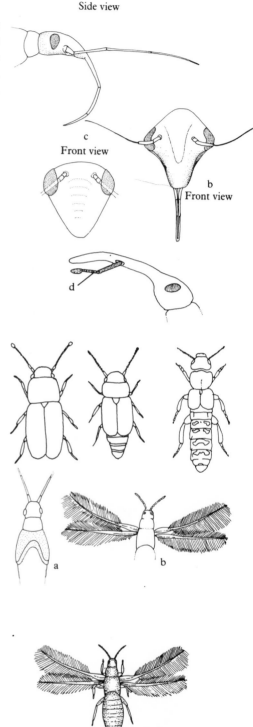

     Note. Some beetles, particularly weevils (family
     Curculionidae) may have the head extended into a
     long snout—the *rostrum* (d). This usually points for-
     wards, but may sometimes be curved under the
     body. These can be separated from the bugs by the
     presence of elbowed antennae which arises some way
     along the rostrum. Also, the forelegs of beetles will
     have four or five tarsal segments, the bugs will have a
     maximum of three.

—   Biting mouthparts. Mouthparts include
     segmented palps . . . . . . **Beetles**
     COLEOPTERA
     (p. 760)

F7   The two pairs of wings are strap-shaped or
     form blunt stubs, with (b) or without (a) a
     fringe of long hairs and lacking obvious
     venation F8

—   The wings are not strap-shaped; they are
     usually fully membranous, with venation,
     but this may be covered in scales and/or
     hairs. F10

F8   Wings are fringed with long hairs . . .
     Thrips, Thunderflies
     THYSANOPTERA
     (p 757)

—   Wings are not fringed with hairs   F9

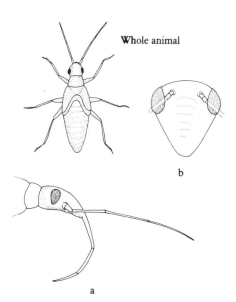

Whole animal

b

a

F9 Mouthparts forming a segmented tube (a). No segmented palps. The tube may be short in which case the head profile will be a characteristic triangular shape when viewed from in front (b). No segmented palps . **nymphal and brachypterous (short-winged) adult Bugs HEMIPTERA** (p. 756)

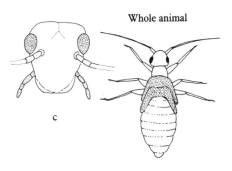

Whole animal

c

— Biting mouthparts; no tube-like structure. Segmented palps present. Head never triangular in profile (c). . . . . . . **nymphal and brachypterous (short-winged) adult Booklice PSOCOPTERA** (p. 756)

F10 Antennae apparently absent, or with less than nine segments F11

— Nine or more antennal segments . F14

F11 Two or three long abdominal "tails" . . **Mayflies EMPHEMEROPTERA** (p. 753)

— No such tails (beware of breakages) F12

F12   Animal more than 21 mm long (measure
       the animals; this is a critical couplet) . .
                Dragonflies & Damselflies
                         ODONATA
                          (p. 754)

—   Animal less than 20 mm long (measure the
       animal; this is a critical couplet) .   .   F13

Whole animals

F13   Mouthparts forming a segmented tube
       (a,b). This may be short, thus forming a
       "beak" which gives the head profile a
       characteristic triangular shape when
       viewed from in front (c). No segmented
       palps .   .   .   .   **Bugs**
                       HEMIPTERA
                          (p. 756)

a
Head: side view

c
Head: front view

b
Head: front view

—   Biting mouthparts. Segmented palps
       usually present F14

F14 Pronotum (the upper plate of the first thoracic segment) well developed, either saddle shaped (a), or extending forwards to cover much of the head (b)   .   .   F15

— Pronotum not as described and illustrated above F16

F15 Hind legs modified for jumping, with greatly enlarged femora (a). Head not covered by the pronotum (b) .   .   .   .   .
Grasshoppers, crickets and ground hoppers
ORTHOPTERA
(p. 755)

— Hind legs not modified for jumping. When seen from above, the head is largely covered by a pronotal shield (c) .   .   .   .
Cockroaches
DICTYOPTERA
(p. 755)

F16 With a sharply constricted "waist" between the thorax and the abdomen; look from the side if you are unsure. Wings never covered in scales, though they may have short hairs F17

— Without a waist between the thorax and the abdomen F18

F17 Tarsi are four- or five-segmented. Wings never held roof-like over the body (a,b)
.   .   .   .   .   . **Bees, ants and wasps**
HYMENOPTERA (Apocrita)
(p. 760)

— Tarsi are two- or three-segmented. Wings held roof-like over the body (c) .   .   F27

F18 Two long abdominal "tails" (cerci).
     Beware of breakages . . . **Stoneflies**
     PLECOPTERA
     (p. 754)

—   Without two long cerci. F19

F19 Wings densely covered in scales or
     obvious hairs between the veins (as well
     as on them); often with reduced venation,
     i.e. only a few cross veins. These features
     may be easier to see with lighting from
     underneath F20

—   Clear wing venation. Wings not covered in
     scales or hairs (though veins may appear
     "hairy") F21

     Note. If there are short hairs sparsely distributed
     between veins, but *no* fringe of hairs around the wing
     margin, then go to couplet F21.

F20 Wings covered in scales and often clearly
     patterned. Mouthparts usually modified
     into a proboscis which may be coiled
     under the body (a). LOOK CLOSELY:
     the scales may be difficult to see except
     under high magnification. Try *gently*
     rubbing a small section of the wing with
     your fingers or a paintbrush to dislodge
     some scales . **Moths and Butterflies**
     LEPIDOPTERA
     (p. 758)

—   Wings are hairy, but not covered in scales.
     Although the wings may be pigmented,
     they are rarely strikingly patterned.
     Mouthparts never form a proboscis (but
     may have long, hairy segmented palps)
     Caddis flies
     TRICHOPTERA
     (p. 758)

     Note. These two groups can be difficult to separate
     in some cases; if in doubt examine the wings under a
     microscope—all moths are covered in scales, though
     these may be reduced in the more primitive groups.

F21 Face forming a long downward pointed "beak" (a); the abdomen of adult males forms a sting-like tail (which is harmless) (b) . . . . **Scorpion flies MECOPTERA** (p. 758)

— Head not particularly extended, not forming a downward pointing "beak". Abdomen never terminating with a "sting-like" tail F22

F22 Front wings with a series of parallel veins running towards their leading edges F23

— Front wings lacking a series of parallel veins running towards their leading edges F25

F23 The front part of the body is elongated, with the combined length of the extended head and first thoracic segment (a) (the prothorax—which does not bear wings) being at least 1.5 times the length of the other two thoracic segments (the meso- and metathorax) together (b). . . . . **Snake flies MEGALOPTERA** (p. 757)

— The front part of the body is not particularly elongated, with the length of the head and prothorax (c) being equal to, or shorter than, the combined length of the hindmost two thoracic segments (d) F24

F24 The outer veins fork before the edges of the wing margins. The prothorax (see above) is distinctly narrower than the other thoracic segments and the head (including the eyes) . . . **Lacewings NEUROPTERA (Sub-Order Planipennia)** (p. 757)

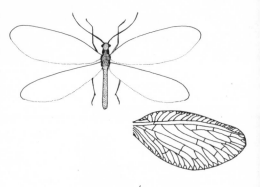

— The hind edge veins do not fork. The prothorax is wide and forms a continuous outline with the head . . **Alder flies MEGALOPTERA** (p. 757)

F25 Complex wing venation (a). More than five "closed" cells in the forewings (see p. 700) F26

— Reduced wing venation (b). Never with more than three, usually only one, "closed" cells in forewings (see p. 700) F27

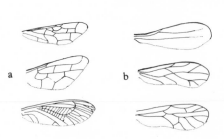

F26 Tarsi three-segmented (or apparently two-segmented). Front wings never with a pigmented stigma on the front edge. Antennae often with more than 20 segments . . . . **Stoneflies PLECOPTERA** (p. 754)

— Tarsi five-segmented. Often with a pigmented stigma on the front edge of the forewings, and the antennae with less than 20 segments . . . . . . **Sawflies HYMENOPTERA (Sub-Order Symphyta)** (p. 760)

F27   Antennae clothed in fine hairs through-
       out. There is a distinct "neck" between
       the head and the thorax. The upper sur-
       face of the thorax and/or abdomen lacks a
       striking banding pattern . . **Booklice**
       PSOCOPTERA
       (p. 756)

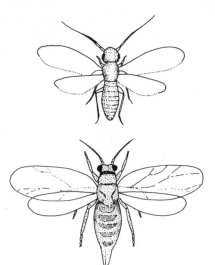

—   Antennae without fine hairs although it
       may have some hairs at the tip. No distinct
       "neck" between head and thorax. Often
       with a striking dark/pale banding pattern
       on the upper thorax and/or abdomen
       Plant lice (bugs)
       HEMIPTERA
       (p. 756)

GENERAL READING

No single text deals with all the invertebrate groups likely to be encountered in British terrestrial habitats. However, the following two books will provide a useful introduction. Cloudsley-Thompson and Sankey (1961) deals with the majority of non-insect groups but is now out-of-date (and difficult to obtain), whilst Chinery's (1986) guide still provides the most comprehensive popular introduction to the insects and is accompanied by excellent colour illustrations. Many other texts deal with invertebrate groups but are restricted, either in the groups included, in the habitats covered or in the accompanying information provided.

Taxonomy

The animal kingdom is divided into a number of major groups known as phyla (singular *phylum*). These are the largest taxonomic groupings and are themselves split up into increasingly smaller taxa as follows:—

Phylum—Class—Order—Family—Genus—Species

There is some disagreement regarding the number of invertebrate phyla, but most biologists agree that there are between 10 and 15. Of these, several live exclusively in marine and/or freshwater aquatic environments, whilst some are restricted to terrestrial habitats outside Britain, usually in the tropics. None of these is included in this guide. Representatives of six phyla of macroscopic invertebrates are likely to be found in British terrestrial habitats and these are listed below, with the taxonomic sub-groups that are involved.

Phylum ASCHELMINTHES (Roundworms)

A very complex group, distinguished from the other worm-like animals by the absence of visible segmentation and their cylindrical bodies. Their identification is extremely difficult and is best left to experts. Two Classes may be encountered in British terrestrial habitats; the Nematoda (round- or eel-worms) and Nematomorpha (hair- or thread-worms). Habitat characters can be a useful way of separating the two classes, with nematodes being widespread whereas the hairworms are restricted to damp soil or thick vegetation in close proximity to freshwater. Also, the vast majority of British species of free-living nematodes rarely reach 1 mm in size whereas the nematomorphans can grow up to 300 mm in length. However, size is not a particularly reliable character—some common nematodes may reach 200 mm. The nematodes are usually pale whereas the hairworms are darker, being coloured light brown to black.

Details of biology and further identification are given in Cloudsley-Thompson & Sankey (1961), Kevan (1962), Goodey (1963) and Jackson & Raw (1966). Identification is very difficult.

Class Nematoda (Eelworms)

Morphology: The eelworms are non-segmented and cylindrical. The majority are less than 1 mm in length but one common species can reach 200 mm.

Ecology: Number of species unknown, possibly many hundreds. Extremely widespread and complex, including parasitic and free-living forms, with a large number alternating between both lifestyles. Many are carnivorous, whilst others feed exclusively on plant juices and bacteria. Most free-living forms are restricted to the soil but the largest British nematode, *Mermis nigrescens,* can be found climbing vegetation on moist spring and summer days. These are egg-laying females. The eggs are ingested by plant eating insects and the hatched young parasitise these hosts which are killed eventually. Maturation is completed in the soil and the life-cycle begins again. By encysting, many nematodes have the ability to suspend their development and remain dormant for long periods in unfavourable conditions. Cysts have remained viable for 15 years in this state.

Further reading: Cloudsley-Thompson & Sankey (1961), Kevan (1962), Goodey (1963), Jackson & Raw (1966).

Class Nematomorpha (Hairworms)

Morphology: Similar to nematodes—also being non-segmented and cylindrical (see the notes above), but hairworms can reach lengths of 300 mm and may be more darkly pigmented.

Ecology: The young parasitise insects, but the adults are free-living in freshwater and in adjacent damp soils. Four British species.

Further reading: Cloudsley-Thompson & Sankey (1961), Kevan (1962), Goodey (1963), Jackson & Raw (1966).

Phylum PLATYHELMINTHES

Generally flattened worms, visually distinguished from the other worms by the absence of true segmentation and their body shape. The phylum includes the parasitic flukes (class Trematoda) and tapeworms (class Cestoda) but its only free-living representatives are Turbellarians.

Class Turbellaria (Free-living Flatworms)

Morphology: The terrestrial species are less flattened than their aquatic counterparts, but have a flattened sole. They lack clear segmentation and are bilaterally symmetrical (equally proportioned on either side of the lengthwise mid-line). Eyes are *either* numerous and scattered around the front (head) end, *or* a pair of larger eyes. The largest British species can reach 90 mm in length, but the most common rarely reaches 25 mm. At least four species are found regularly in damp woods, etc.

Ecology: Predominantly an aquatic group but seven species have been recorded in damp terrestrial habitats—in shady moist woods, under logs, in decaying vegetation and leaf litter, or in damp moss. Very little is known of their biology. The most common species—*Microplana terrestris*—is most likely to be found on moist nights, whereas the remaining species are more strictly subterranean and are only rarely recorded above the ground. The flatworms are carnivorous, feeding on minute molluscs and worms and can be found at most times of the year.

Further details of biology and identification are given in Ball & Reynoldson (1981).

Phylum NEMERTEA (Ribbon worms)

Non-segmented and difficult to distinguish from flatworms (class Turbellaria; see above). The two groups were combined as one by early naturalists and nemerteans are still sometimes regarded as a class within the phylum Platyhelminthes. One British representative occurs in terrestrial habitats. Argonemertes dendyi *has an eversible proboscis which will distinguish live specimens from closely similar flatworms (see notes above). Up to 25 mm long. Also, the eyes in this species are arranged in two groups of 3 or 8. This contrasts with the arrangement in flatworms. Two stripes run lengthways along the whole of the body whereas in flatworms which share a similar pattern the stripes usually merge or become indistinct some way short of the head end.*

Ecology: A dendyi *lives in damp shady places, usually under stones and wood in dense copses and near streams. Recorded from Ireland, Wales and the south coast of England. It is thought to be a predator on immature and soil-dwelling insects (including springtails, bugs and myriapods), feeding by everting its proboscis and sucking the juices of its prey.*

Further details are given in Pantin (1969) and Gibson (1982).

Phylum ANNELIDA

This group contains those worms which are segmented. Terrestrial species are never flattened.

Class Hirudinea (Leeches)

Morphology: Many-segmented worms which have suckers at each end of the body. A common species on land—*Haemopsis sanguisuga*—can reach 50 mm in length.

Ecology: No British leech is truly terrestrial, the only land-dwelling forms being found in damp tropical habitats. However, two British species (*H. sanguisuga* and *Trocheta subviridis*) are amphibious and may be found considerable distances from their aquatic homes, sometimes in gardens, usually under stones or in the soil. The amphibious leeches are carnivorous, feeding on small insects, worms and slugs. They do not suck blood and are harmless to humans. Although some aquatic leeches do leave water they are restricted to banks and soil very close to the water's edge.

Further details of ecology and identification are given in Mann (1962 & 1964) and Elliott & Mann (1979).

Class Oligochaeta (Earthworms and Whiteworms (= Potworms))

Morphology: Soft bodied worms with obvious external segmentation. In adults, some segments are broadened and slightly fused to form a band (the clitellum). Two families are represented in terrestrial habitats: the earthworms (family Lumbricidae) and the potworms (family Enchytraeidae). The latter are usually pale in colour and rarely reach 25 mm, whereas the earthworms may be heavily pigmented and can reach 250 mm in length.

Ecology: Most of the terrestrial worms live exclusively in the soil, but can be found in dense and moist leaf litter or decaying vegetation. Some species do protrude and emerge from the ground at night when optimum temperatures and humidity occur. The common earthworm—*Lumbricus terrestris*—is unusual in that it also mates on the surface. A vertical stratification may occur in the soil, with different species of earthworm being found in zones of increasing depth. Pot-worms are unable to burrow and are largely restricted in movement to fissures and crevices, or burrows made by other animals. All worms avoid the surface during daylight hours. They can achieve high numbers. Some populations reaching 850 individuals per surface square metre of soil. They feed on organic detritus (dead leaves, twigs, etc.). Life cycles, and frequency of occurrence at different times of the year, varies between species.

Edwards & Lofty (1972) and Sims & Gerard (1985) give further information on biology and identification of earthworms. O'Connor (1967) provides a detailed introduction to the enchytraeids.

Phylum ARTHROPODA

This phylum contains over 80% of the animals described so far, world-wide—over one and a quarter million species. The main distinguishing features are the hardened external skeleton with three or more pairs of tubular, jointed legs. Three sub-divisions (sub-phyla) are recognised—the trilobites, chelicerates and mandibulates. The former are extinct, but representatives of the latter two can be found in British terrestrial habitats. Cloudsley-Thompson & Sankey (1961) give a general introduction to the biology and taxonomy of non-insect groups, whilst Chinery (1986) does the same for the insect orders.

Sub-phylum Chelicerata

This group is distinguished from the sub-phylum Mandibulata by the absence of antennae. Also, the head and thorax are fused whereas in the mandibulates these two parts of the body are separate. Their name is derived from the specialised front appendages which form claws, or chelae, *although these are not always obvious. Only one class, the Arachnida, has successfully invaded the land and is represented by five orders in Britain. Jones (1984) serves as a useful introduction to the group as a whole, and Cloudsley-Thompson & Sankey (1961) cover all groups with the exception of the scorpions.*

Class Arachnida

Mainly predators with over 50,000 species worldwide. Four pairs of legs; no antennae; no wings. See Cloudsley-Thompson & Sankey (1961) and Jones (1984).

Order Scorpionida (Scorpions)

Morphology: The head and thorax are fused and are covered by a single shield (the carapace*). The front appendages have been modified into powerful chelicerae and a pair of large claws. The abdomen is extended into a narrowing tail terminating with a sting. Four pairs of walking legs. The poison gland is located in the sting, but the British representative—*Euscorpius flavicaudis—*is harmless to humans and rarely exceeds 40 mm in length. Live young are carried on the abdomen of their mother until they have moulted, after which they disperse. The immatures are easily recognisable as scorpions.*

Ecology: Unlike other arachnid orders—the spiders, mites and pseudoscorpions—the scorpions do not have silk glands and are unable to spin webs or weave egg sacs or refuges. They have poor sight and are primarily nocturnal, spending the day resting in crevices in walls or under stone. Euscorpius flavicaudis *has been found at Sheerness in Kent for over 100 years.*

See Wanless (1977) for further details.

Order Pseudoscorpionida ("False" scorpions)

Morphology: have large claws, but lack the abdominal tail and sting which are characteristic of the true scorpions. Poison glands are contained in the claws. The largest British species reach only 4 mm. The young are carried on the mother's abdomen and disperse only after moulting. They cannot be confused with any other group.

Ecology: Active predators, feeding on minute animals such as psocids (see p. 756) and collembola (see p. 753). Most occur in moss, leaf litter, the top layer of soil or under stones and loose bark. Two of the 25 British species are found in houses, where they feed on other arthropods including house mites and bed bugs. Pseudoscorpions have been found clinging to other insects, but this is not a parasitic relationship—the "hosts" are being used simply for transport, a practice known as phoresy.

The key by Evans & Browning (1954) is the only fully-comprehensive guide to British represen-tatives, but is now out-of-date. General information is given by Cloudsley-Thompson & Sankey (1961) and Jones (1984). A new synopsis, by G. Legg, is in preparation.

Order Araneae (Spiders)

Morphology: Distinguished from other arachnids by the presence of a narrow waist—the pedicel. *The hind end lacks the obvious segmentation characteristic of all other arachnid groups with the exception of the mites and ticks (see Acari, below). Following hatching, the young undergo a series of moults becoming increasingly like their parents. However, even the most immature spiders are unlikely to be confused with any other group.*

Ecology: An enormously diverse group, with nearly 600 species in Britain. Mainly predators or other arthropods, predominantly insects. Spiders have the ability to spin silk but this is used to a varying extent. Some spin webs to catch prey, others only use the silk to manufacture refuges or protective sacs for their eggs. The silk may also be used as a means of transport. Smaller spiders spin fine threads which are caught in air-currents carrying the spiders to considerable heights and for large distances. This practice, known as ballooning, ensures that spiders are often the first animals to colonise a new site and can be found in habitats throughout the whole of Britain.

Bristowe (1958) provides a useful introduction to natural history of the British fauna; the keys in three volumes by Locket & Millidge (1951 & 1953) and Locket, Millidge & Merrett (1974) cover all British species, but the books by Jones (1984) and Roberts (Vols 1 & 3, 1985: Vol 2, 1987) provide comprehensive up-dates, with colour pictures. An AIDGAP key to families of British spiders is to be published (Jones-Walters, in preparation).

Order Opiliones (Harvestmen)

Morphology: Harvestmen lack the waist of the spiders and are usually also distinguished by the presence of visible segmentation on the lower abdomen (although this may be indistinct in some species). They usually have a wart-like tubercle—the ocularium—*on the upper side of the carapace, on which the eyes are situated. In most species, the walking legs are very long, extending to several* times the body length, but they are much shorter in some groups inhabiting leaf-litter. The young start moulting almost immediately after hatching and this is repeated seven or eight times before reaching maturity, but even at the youngest stages most nymphs will be recognisable as harvestmen.

Ecology: All of the British Harvestmen are predominantly carnivorous, feeding on a variety of invertebrates, usually through active nocturnal predation but also whilst scavenging. They do not use webs for trapping. Twenty-six species occur in Britain. The group is widespread, occurring throughout Britain and in most terrestrial habitats. Representatives can be found at any time of the year.

Biology and identification are covered by Sankey & Savory (1974).

Order Acari (Mites and Ticks)

Morphology: Almost all free-living Acari are smaller than 2 mm, displaying an enormous variation in external appearance. They can be distinguished from spiders by the absence of a waist, and from harvestmen by the absence of both the external segmentation and the ocularium. Most species of mites and ticks possess an obvious head region, the capitulum. The life-history stages are still uncertain for most species, but the majority of acari hatch as six-legged larvae which are usually followed by one or more eight-legged nymphal stages, before becoming sexually-mature adults. Some mites live exclusively in plant galls—these may have only two pairs of legs. The number of larval and nymphal instars (stages between moults), and the external form that they take may vary as a result of habitat condition at that time. Similarly, the developmental stages can be either parasitic or free-living.

Ecology: Over 1500 species of mites and ticks have been recorded in Britain and many more remain to be found. A great variety of lifestyles have been developed; even within the same species the life-history stages may have a contrasting ecology. The ticks are ectoparasitic acari which feed on vertebrate blood but spend most of the time in vegetation, attaching themselves to their hosts only when feeding. Likewise, most other groups have representatives which are parasitic at some stage in their life-cycle. This parasitism may have developed through the phoretic behaviour of many mites, whereby they hitch lifts on the bodies of other animals (see also the notes on pseudoscorpions). Whilst a large number of acari are carnivorous, mainly feeding through parasitism and scavenging rather than active predation, some species are predominantly plant feeders often through sucking the sap of their hosts. Spider mites may cause considerable damage to horticultural crops in this way, while some mites spread virus diseases and cause galls. The oribatid mites are usually the most abundant group of arthropods in litter and soil, feeding on decaying organic matter and associated fungi and bacteria. Acari are widespread, forming an important part of the invertebrate fauna in most habitats—one estimate was for 500 million mites per acre in some British grasslands.

Cloudsley-Thompson & Sankey (1961) provide an introduction to the group, but Evans et al. (1961) give a fully-comprehensive coverage, whilst Arthur (1963) deals with the ticks alone.

Sub-phylum Mandibulata

In very simplified terms the mandibulates are distinguished from the sub-phylum Chelicerata by having antennae, and lacking the chelicerae that characterise the latter group. The mandibulates can be divided into two groups: the primarily aquatic (Crustacea) and the primarily terrestrial (Insecta and Myriapoda).

Class Crustacea

The crustaceans are distinguished from the terrestrial mandibulata by having two pairs of antennae (although one pair is very inconspicuous in woodlice) and differently structured appendages. Although predominantly aquatic animals, three groups—the orders Isopoda, Amphipoda and Copepoda—are represented in British terrestrial habitats.

Order Isopoda (Woodlice)

Morphology: Woodlice are only likely to be confused with one other group, the pill millipedes (see below) but can be distinguished from the latter by their having a number of narrow segments at the hind end with projecting appendages (the uropods). The uropods are difficult to see in the pillbug woodlice, Armadillidium spp. They are flattened, with seven pairs of walking legs as adults. However, very young larvae (which hatch in a late stage of development) may have the last pair of *legs incomplete. Woodlice have rudimentary abdominal gills, a legacy from the aquatic existence which is characteristic of the crustacea as a whole. The gills, although being protected by plates which hide them from view, are still prone to water loss and this restricts most of these animals to humid habitats and a nocturnal lifestyle. An increasing specialisation to terrestrial life can be seen across the various representatives, the better adapted groups being more able to remain active during daylight hours.*

Ecology: Forty-two species of woodlice have been recorded in Britain. All are scavengers, feeding on dead or dying plant material, and their own droppings (thus increasing the efficiency of the digestive process). Most are nocturnal and found in humid habitats. The eggs are carried by the mother until they hatch. The young resemble the adults but may lack a pair of legs; these early stages are often found in broods which are attended by the mother until later stages of development. Woodlice can be found at any time of the year.

Full details of biology and identification are given by Sutton (1972), recently updated by Harding & Sutton (1985).

Order Amphipoda (Sand hoppers and Scuds)

Morphology: Up to 15 mm long. Shrimp-like: compressed side-to-side and curled up (usually). Eleven pairs of "legs", but these are specialised into walking, swimming and jumping appendages. Two pairs of antennae. The relative length of the antennae will help to separate these from the aquatic amphipods. The upper pair are clearly shorter than the lower pair, their whole length being shorter than the peduncle (the enlarged basal segments) of the lower antennae. The lower antennae are approximately half as long as the rest of the body.

Ecology: Only one truly terrestrial British species, Arcitalitrus (Talitroides) dorrieni. *(Other members of the same family—the Talitridae—are semi-terrestrial. Although never fully submerged, they are restricted to the supra-littoral zone on or near the seashore; sand dunes, salt marshes, etc.).* A. dorrieni *is usually found in damp or decaying vegetation, or humus. These animals are probably scavengers but may feed on carrion also. Recorded from the Isles of Scilly originally, but now found in many inland habitats throughout southwest Britain and in isolated localities as far apart as Surrey, Argyll and Co. Galway (Ireland).*

Identification and further details are given in Lincoln (1979).

Order Copepoda

Morphology: Less than 1 mm. Two pairs of antennae; the upper one longer than the lower. The larvae, known as nauplii, are free living and have three pairs of appendages on hatching. Further pairs of legs are added during a series of moults.

Ecology: Little is known, but the terrestrial copepods are likely to feed on decomposing organic matter. They can secrete a slime coating to form a cyst and survive long periods of frost and drought. May be abundant in moist beech litter in Southern England.

Further information on this group is given by Gurney (1931) and by Harding & Smith (1960).

Class Pauropoda

Morphology: Very small, 0.5 to 2 mm; blind; with uniquely branched antennae; body adorned with pairs of long bristles; ten pairs of legs when adult, but the tiny nymphs (less than 0.2 mm long) hatch with three pairs of legs and only attain the full complement after a series of moults.

Ecology: Very common in soil, but frequently overlooked because of their size. They are thought to feed on dead plant material. Life cycle and population biology are largely unknown, but they can be found throughout Britain at any time of the year.

Class Diplopoda (Millipedes)

Morphology: With few exceptions, the millipedes have long bodies (up to 50 mm), several times longer than broad. Some are almost circular in cross section and this will help to distinguish them from the more flattened centipedes. They also lack the anterior claws (the *forcipules*—see overleaf) of the latter, and have two pairs of legs per body segment compared to a single pair in centipedes. They will also have less than 10 antennal segments, whereas centipedes have more. Some groups have over 80 pairs of legs. Unfortunately, the adults of some groups do not conform to the general description. Pill millipedes (Glomerida) may be confused with woodlice, but lack the complex segmentation at the rear of the abdomen. The spiny *Polyxenus lagurus* (Polyxenida) is not "typical" but does have millipede characters when examined closely. Others have keels on the side of each segment, giving a flat-backed appearance (Polydesmida: Chordeumatida (so. Craspedoso-matidea)), and are often confused with centipedes but can be separated by the double-pairs of legs, the absence of a pair of claws (forcipules) and the antennal segmentation.

The larvae hatch with three (or four) pairs of legs and gain their full complement after a number of moults. The early stage could be confused with minute soil-dwelling insects, particularly springtails. Millipede larvae will rarely have only six abdominal segments, will not have antennae originating from the upper side of the face, nor will they have any ventral tubes or springing organs; springtails will have one or more of these characters.

Ecology: Fifty-two British species. Mainly soil or leaf litter dwellers, but will use other habitats opportunistically. For example, cow pats and manure will often provide temporary homes for large numbers of millipedes. All are detritivores, feeding on dead plant material, but some species will feed on fungi and dead animals, whilst others will crop fresh vegetation. In drought, the latter may infest arable crops and can become pests.

Blower (1985) gives detailed information on millipede biology, and takes identification to species level.

Class Chilopoda (Centipedes)
Morphology: Very variable in size (up to 80 mm), and morphology. The flattened body form, and presence of claws (the forcipules) at the head end, will distinguish the centipedes from millipedes. Also, the latter have two pairs of legs per body segment whereas centipedes have one pair only. Centipedes have more than 14 antennal segments, often many more. The number of legs in adults varies between the three orders, from a minimum of 15 pairs to over one hundred (see below).

Immature geophilomorph centipedes hatch with a full complement of legs, but in the other two orders the larvae have a reduced number, four or five pairs, and additional pairs are added as the animals undergo a series of moults before maturation.

Ecology: Forty-seven British species. The centipedes are prone to water loss and the majority are nocturnal predators, favouring humid habitats. They may take refuge deep underground, or in crevices during droughts and hard winters; otherwise, they can be found at all times of the year. Prey are actively caught, being immobilised with the aid of a poison gland situated at the base of the claws (British species are harmless to humans). The behaviour of each of the three orders is quite distinctive, as is their morphology. The burrowing centipedes (Geophilomorpha) are blind and have long flexible bodies, with relatively short legs, whereas the surface hunters (Lithobiomorpha and Scolopendromorpha) are able to see, and have stouter and less flexible bodies with longer legs which enable these animals to travel at speed along the ground, using visual cues to seek out their prey, usually surface-dwelling insects.

A full review of the British centipedes' biology, and keys to identification of species, are given in Eason (1964). Lewis (1981) provides a review of the biology of the group.

Class Symphyla
Morphology: Can reach 10 mm in length, usually smaller than 4 mm. Long, thread-like antennae composed of many segments. White. Similar to centipedes, but adults have a maximum of 12 pairs of legs and lack the claws. Juveniles hatch without the full complement of legs, usually six pairs, and add further pairs during the three months taken to reach maturity.

Ecology: Common in upper layers of the soil, feeding mainly on dead plant material. They will feed on living roots and in artificial situations, in greenhouses for example, they may become pests.

Class Insecta
A huge group, with over one million species world-wide. The recorded number of British species rises almost daily, but already exceeds 20,000. Insects have successfully invaded all terrestrial habitats. Adults usually have three pairs of legs, with three major body divisions—the head, thorax and abdomen. Antennae are usually present. The primitive orders—belonging to the sub-class *Apterygota*—lack wings, but the more advanced orders—in the sub-class *Pterygota*—may have one, or two pairs (though some species may be secondarily wingless). The Pterygota can itself be divided according to life-history development: the *Exopterygota* has young stages—called *nymphs*—in which wings develop externally, which usually resemble the adults; the *Endopterygota* have wings which develop internally and the immatures—"true" *larvae*—are clearly different from the adults, often appearing maggot- or caterpillar-like.

Two texts are particularly recommended: Imms (1977) gives a comprehensive introduction to the biology of the group as a whole, whilst Chinery (1986) is extremely useful for identification, and includes a large number of excellent colour plates.

Order Protura

Morphology: Tiny, less than 2 mm long; pointed head; blind; antennae, if present, very short; pale; 12 abdominal segments in adults, but only nine in recently hatched nymphs. Others are added later, a developmental feature which is unique to proturans amongst insects, but is common in the Pauropoda, Diplopoda, Chilopoda and Symphyla (pp. 751–752).

Ecology: Twelve British species. All are soil dwellers, where they may be abundant, but are also common in leaf litter. Widespread. They are thought to be scavengers, feeding on dead or dying plant and animal material. Their biology is not well known but although some species are at their most active during the summer, others will be found throughout the year.

Further information and identification is given by Nosek (1973).

Order Thysanura (Three-pronged bristletails, Silverfish, Firebrats, etc.)

Morphology: Cone-shaped body; three long tails; thread-like antennae. Body covered in scales, and may appear silvery. Movement is often sinuous—hence the popular name, "silverfish". The immature nymphs resemble the adults. The largest reach 20 mm in length, but most are smaller.

Ecology: Nine species. The three-tailed bristletails live in a wide range of habitats, including buildings, heathlands and rocky shores (sea cliffs), and feed mainly on dying vegetation and detritus. The house-dwellers (including the firebrat) favour starchy foods. Although the "wild-living" forms do seem to have seasonal life-cycles, eggs being laid in late-summer/autumn and hatching in the following spring/early summer, the domestic species can lay and hatch at any time of the year.

Delaney (1954) gives further details of biology and identification.

Order Diplura (Two-pronged bristletails)

Morphology: Small, 3–5 mm; usually white; two tails; thorax clearly divided into three segments; no compound eyes. The nymphs resemble the adults.

Ecology: Eleven British species all belonging to one genus Campodea. *Widely distributed, in leaf litter and soil, under stones and in any habitat where plant debris is common. They are thought to prey on springtails (Collembola), dead animals and roots. Little is known of their life-history; they breed in the summer but are found throughout the year.*

Delaney (1954) gives further details of biology and identification.

Order Collembola (Springtails)

Morphology: Small, up to 5 mm but usually smaller. External appearance varies, but always with a distinctive six-segmented abdomen. The surface dwellers are larger, with longer antennae and legs, often with a forked springing organ and wart-like tube underneath the abdomen. The soil inhabitants have very short legs and antennae and lack the springing organ and tube, and many are tiny (smaller than 1 mm), pale and blind. The nymphs resemble the adults, but are smaller.

Ecology: Approximately 300 British species. Springtails live in soil, leaf litter, grass swards, etc., feeding on dead or dying plant material. They are extremely abundant; one scientist estimated 230 million individuals per acre of meadowland. The biology of this group is largely unknown, but adults and nymphs can be found at any time of the year.

The texts by Gisin (1960) (in German) and Fjellberg (1892) take identification further, but some expertise and suitable equipment is needed.

Order Ephemeroptera (Mayflies)

Morphology: Adults usually have two or three long tails. Although most have two pairs of wings, the hind pair is much smaller and is missing in some species. The antennae are short, being scarcely longer than the width of the head at most. The subimago—a developmental stage between nymph and adult which is unique to the mayflies—resembles the adult but has dull and opaque wings which are fringed with short hairs. Also, the tail bristles and legs may be shorter than in the adult stage.

Ecology: Forty-seven British species. Widely distributed. Eggs are laid in water, and the nymphs are entirely aquatic. The earliest species begin to emerge from water around May—hence the name.

The length of time spent in the subimaginal stage varies between species, from several hours to many weeks, and is extended in colder conditions. The adult stages often last only two or three days, during which they may not feed. Both can fly, but the subimago is often found sheltering in vegetation near the water's edge. Male mayflies may swarm at certain times of year, particularly during summer evenings.

Macan (1969) and Elliot & Humpesch (1983) give full details of biology and identification.

Order Odonata (Dragonflies and Damselflies)

Morphology: Often large (up to 80 mm in overall length). Head is wide, with large globular eyes. Antennae are short, never longer than half the width of the head. The two pairs of wings are fully membranous, and may be pigmented. The order is divided into two sub-orders: s.o. Zygoptera (damselflies) and s.o. Anisoptera (dragonflies). Damselflies have both wings similar in size and shape, folded back over the abdomen when at rest, with eyes which are clearly separated when viewed from above the head. Dragonflies have broader hind wings, and both pairs are held out sideways when at rest. The eyes actually meet, or nearly do so, on top of the head.

Ecology: Although dragonflies (24 British spp.) and damselflies (18 spp.) can be found in a wide range of habitats, they are often restricted to the vicinity of freshwater or wetlands in which they breed. Several species may now be extinct because suitable habitats have disappeared, as a result of physical disturbance or pollution. The nymphal stage is entirely aquatic and may last several years but the adult is short-lived, only surviving for one week on average, although many will live to three weeks and some as long as eight weeks. The adults are encountered most often on hot, sunny days between June and September, and are least numerous in cold, wet summers. All are carnivorous, actively preying on flying insects.

Corbet et al. (1960), Keen (1977), Hammond (1985), Aguilar et al. (1986), Gibbons (1986) and McGeery (1986) include comprehensive details for the identification and natural history of the group.

Order Plecoptera (Stoneflies)

Morphology: Usually have two pairs of wings, with the hind pair being larger, but in some males these can be reduced in size. The wings are usually tightly folded over their flattened body, but in some species may be laid flat. Two tails are present in some, but not all, species. The antennae are long; as long as the body in many species.

Ecology: Thirty-four British species. Widespread, but most common near stony streams. The nymphs are aquatic but most are restricted to oxygen-rich waters and as such are useful indicators of contamination. Stoneflies can fly, particularly on sunny days, but often prefer to run when disturbed. The adults, which may only live for two or three weeks, are thought to feed on lichens and algae (if at all).

Hynes (1977) gives full details of biology and identification, and practical information is given by Macan (1982).

Order Phasmida (Stick insects)

Morphology: Unmistakeable. Often large (up to 90 mm), slender insects. Nymphs resemble adults.

Ecology: There are no native British species but, because of their popularity as laboratory insects and pets, escapees may be found in gardens or school grounds, etc. Some colonies survive in greenhouses. Vegetarian. Nocturnal.

Information on biology and identification is given in Ragge (1965), and Chinery (1986).

Order Dermaptera (Earwigs)

Morphology: Up to 25 mm long, but usually less than 17 mm; long thread-like antennae, with 50+ segments; shortened wing cases which cover a second pair of membranous wings; two curved pincers, though these are only slightly curved in nymphs and some adult females. Nymphs resemble adults, but lack the wing cases (and a strong curve in their "pincers"). The youngest, and smallest, nymphs are attended by their mother.

Ecology: Seven British species. Widespread, but prefer to rest in dark crevices during the daylight—hence their English name. Most can fly and may be taken in light traps at night. Smaller species measure less than 5 mm when fully grown and are easily overlooked. Feed primarily on plant material, but may be omnivorous, sometimes preying on small arthropods. Earwigs are less likely to be found in winter months during which adults hibernate: in subterranean retreats; on fence post; under *bark, etc. Nymphs are mainly encountered during spring but will be found at any time of the year. Hincks (1956) and Brindle (1977) give further information, and identification to species.*

Order Dictyoptera (Cockroaches)

Morphology: Sometimes large (up to 35 mm), flattened insects, with a large pronotum which projects forwards covering most of the head. Antennae are long and threadlike, usually as long as the body. Biting mouthparts; never with piercing mouthparts. May be winged or wingless. The hind end of the abdomen terminates with two stout "tails". Although the earliest immatures are worm-like they moult almost immediately after hatching and the subsequent nymphal stages resemble the adults.

Ecology: Although 9 species are found in Britain, most are restricted to heated buildings and outhouses. Only three are truly "native", outdoor-living, species and these are most likely to be encountered in Southern England. All are nocturnal omnivorous scavengers. Move rapidly when disturbed. Domestic species can be found at all times of the year, at any stage in the life cycle. The life cycle of the outdoor species is largely unknown, but they are thought to overwinter as eggs, or late-stage nymphs, and reach maturity in May/June, mating soon thereafter and dying towards the end of the year.

Ragge (1965) gives detailed information on biology and identification of the British species.

Order Orthoptera (Grasshoppers, Crickets and Ground hoppers)

Morphology: A diverse group, both in size (body length up to 50 mm) and body form. However, all have well-developed back legs which are clearly suited for jumping, and the majority have a well developed saddle-shaped pronotum. They may be winged, with the first of the two pairs sometimes being thick and "leathery" in the basal part. Many have rudimentary wings, whilst others are completely wingless. Metamorphosis is incomplete; nymphs, although "worm-like" for a short time after hatching, moult quickly and resemble the mature forms.

Six distinctive families may be encountered. The bush crickets *(family Tettigonidae) have long thread-like antennae, always considerably longer than the body length, with the legs terminating in four-segmented tarsi. Females have a large, curved ovipositor.* Crickets *(family Gryllidae) also have long thread-like antennae, and large ovipositors, but have three-segmented tarsi.* Grasshoppers *(family Acrididae) have short, thick antennae, which are half as long as the body at most, as do* ground hoppers *(family Tetrigidae), but the latter can be separated easily by the form of the pronotum. This is very large in ground hoppers and extends backwards to cover most of the abdomen. Two other families are encountered rarely. The* mole crickets *(family Gryllotalpidae) have short antennae which are one third as long as the body at most, and greatly enlarged fore legs. The wingless* camel crickets *(family Rhaphidophoridae) have long antennae, but also have two exeptionally long abdominal "tails", in addition to the ovipositor in females. These are as long as the pronotum, which is never true for other families.*

Ecology: Camel crickets *(1 spp.) and* mole crickets *(1 spp.) are very rare. The former is restricted to greenhouses, the latter to a few sites in Southern England (and the Channel Islands). The* grasshoppers *(11 spp.) are widely distributed, as are* ground hoppers *(3 spp.), but* bush crickets *(10 spp.) are mainly restricted to the southern half of England.* Crickets *(4 spp.) are increasingly rare, and are only likely to be found in the extreme South of England. Adults of all groups are most common in the summer, but whereas grasshoppers and bush crickets overwinter (November–May) as eggs, ground hoppers and crickets may "hibernate" as late-stage nymphs. The diet of grasshoppers and ground hoppers is exclusively vegetarian, the former feeding primarily on grasses, the latter on algae and mosses. Although most bush crickets are also herbivorous, some are known to be carnivorous. Activity rhythms also differ. Grasshoppers and ground hoppers are most active during the day, whereas bush crickets are particularly active at night. Grasshoppers, crickets and bush crickets have characteristic "songs", produced by rubbing legs and/or wings together, and these can be used to identify the groups. These songs have been recorded and are available on the record which accompanied Ragge's (1965) book which remains the most comprehensive introduction to the biology and identification of the Orthoptera (but also includes Phasmida and Dictyoptera, see opposite and above); unfortunately, both are now very difficult to obtain. A full revision, with an accompanying cassette, is to be published. (Marshall & Haes, in preparation; anticipated publication early 1988). Brown (1983) provides a useful, and readily available, synopsis for the grasshoppers and bush crickets.*

Order Psocoptera (Book- and Bark-lice)

Morphology: Small, up to 6 mm. Booklice can be winged (alate) or wingless (apterous). Antennae are long and thread-like. In wingless forms the nymphs resemble adults and can only be distinguished by two-segmented tarsi compared to the three segments found after maturation (although some adults also have only two tarsal segments). In winged forms the nymphs have fleshy wing pads which lack venation whereas the adults' wings are fully membranous and veined. Psocids may be confused with some bugs (Hemiptera), and small sawflies and wasps (Hymenoptera). Bugs will have piercing mouth-parts whereas psocids' are of the biting type. The wing venation and number of tarsal segments will distinguish the psocids from the Hymenoptera.

Ecology: Fifty species are thought to be native to Britain, but a further 40 have also been found. Many are tree-dwellers, but some live indoors. Microflora—small fungi, pollen grains, etc—are the main food source, but house-dwellers feed on moulds growing on old books, thus giving this group their name. Nymphs resemble adults, but lack fully developed wings and/or tarsal segments (see above). Psocids can be found at all times of the year.

New (1974) gives further details of the group's biology and takes identification to species level.

Order Phthiraptera (True lice)

This group is divided into two distinct sub-orders:—

A. Sub-order Mallophaga (Biting lice)

Morphology: Adults less than 6 mm long, rarely more than 3 mm. The body is flattened side-to-side. Antennae inconspicuous, eyes reduced or absent, wings missing. Biting mouthparts. The head is as wide as, or wider than, the broadest part of the thorax. The nymphs are similar, but smaller, and also spend their lives on the host.

Ecology: Approximately 400 British species. All are external parasites on birds and mammals, feeding on hair, feathers and, sometimes, blood. They will die within a few hours of leaving a host, and are unlikely to be found far from a body. Species are restricted by their hosts' distribution, rather than geographical factors, and many are found worldwide. They may be found at any time of the year.

Further information and identification is given by Clay (1969 & 1970).

B. Sub-order Anoplura (Sucking lice)

Morphology: Rarely larger than 3 mm. Antennae short, eyes inconspicuous, wings absent. Differ from Mallophaga in having a narrow head, narrower than the thorax, and having fused thoracic segments. Also, the mouthparts are adapted for sucking rather than biting. The nymphs resemble adults.

Ecology: Approximately 25 British species. External parasites on mammals, including man, and can be important disease carriers (e.g. of typhus fever). They are unable to survive away from a host but can be found throughout the year.

Like the biting lice (Mallophaga, see above) anoplurans are found everywhere, their occurrence reflecting the distribution of their hosts rather than geography. Keys are applicable worldwide, e.g. Ferris (1961).

Order Hemiptera (Bugs)

Morphology: A large group including a wide range of forms. Most can be distinguished from other insect groups by their sucking mouthparts, but these are reduced, or missing altogether (e.g. male scale insects), from some Hemiptera. The Order is separated into two sub-Orders; the Homoptera and the Heteroptera. The fore wings of the former are uniform throughout, being either entirely membranous (e.g. aphids, psyllids, scale insects) or entirely hardened (or leathery) (e.g. the hoppers). In contrast, only the tips of the forewings in Heteroptera are membranous, the basal part being hardened or leathery (e.g. shield bugs, lace bugs, damsel bugs, water bugs). In some groups the wings may be missing, or reduced to short wing pads. Antennal form also varies between groups. The scale insects and mealy bugs are the most likely to cause confusion. The females, sometimes legless as well as wingless, may appear grub-like, whilst males have one pair of wings and no sucking mouthparts. The abdominal appendages, lack of wing venation and long antennae will separate the latter from other groups. Metamorphosis in Hemiptera is incomplete, with nymphs becoming increasingly like wingless adults. However, the transition from nymph to adult may be quite sudden in some groups such as the whiteflies. Wing pads usually appear just before maturity.

Ecology: Nearly 1800 British species. The vast majority are sucking insects, feeding on a wide range of vegetation. Many are crop pests. A few are active predators, whilst others are blood suckers (e.g. Bed Bugs). Adults are found throughout the year, but mainly between spring and autumn.

Further reading and identification: the most comprehensive text for heteroptera is by Southwood & Leston (1959), whilst keys in Volume 2 of the Royal Entomological Society's "Handbooks" series enables identification to species level in some groups of homoptera.

Order Thysanoptera (Thrips)

Morphology: Small, usually less than 3 mm long. Moderately long antennae, often as long as the width of the head. Piercing mouthparts—but these are not obvious. Long and slender body, with habit of·curving abdomen upwards when disturbed. Wings (if present) appear as narrow straps fringed with long hairs. Nymphs or, very rarely, active pupae, may have hairless wing pads and may be confused with Psocoptera (booklice), but the shorter antennae and the lack of a "neck" will distinguish the thrips. Apart from the lack of fully developed wings, and having fewer antennal and tarsal segments, nymphs resemble adults except in colour. Nymphs are generally creamy white or yellow, while adults are invariably darker—usually brownish black.

Ecology: Approximately 158 British species. Mainly plant sap feeders, but some may be predators. Some are crop pests. Thysanoptera may fly in large numbers in humid conditions; hence their other common name—thunder flies.

Further reading and identification are given in Lewis (1973) and Mound et al. (1976).

Order Neuroptera (Lacewings)

Morphology: This Order includes the typical lacewings and the family Coniopterygidae. With one exception (the Coniopterygidae) adult Neuropterans can be distinguished by their two pairs of similar wings with complex venation, long antennae, large compound eyes and absence of any abdominal tails. Coniopterygidae do not conform to the normal lacewing pattern; briefly, the adults are small insects (less than 8 mm long), are covered in white powdery wax and have dissimilar sized wings with reduced venation. As with lacewings the larvae undergo complete metamorphosis and do not resemble the adults. They differ from the lacewing larvae by having hairy (plumose) antennae and by lacking the strongly projecting jaws; nevertheless, as with lacewing larvae, their jaws are adapted for sucking (adults in both groups have biting mouthparts). The larval palps are often club-shaped. Length is usually less than 2.5 mm. Adult lacewings have two pairs of similar sized wings, with complex wing venation including parallel leading edge veins and forking at the wing margins. Lacewing larvae are similar in general body shape to the Coniopterygidae larvae, but differ in antennae, which are never plumose, and mouthparts, which never have club-shaped palps (see above). They are often larger, reaching 15 mm in length.

Ecology: The Coniopterygidae (7 British spp.) and lacewings (47 spp.) are predators, both as larvae and as adults, and are known to take a wide range of small invertebrate prey including aphids. Lacewing adults may also feed on nectar and honeydew—the sugary excretion from aphids. Adults are mainly active at dawn and dusk and will be found resting on vegetation during the day, sometimes in groups. Deciduous woods, and vegetation near rivers and streams, are favoured habitats. The life cycle is not seasonal and overwintering may occur at any stage.

Further details for identification and biology are given in Fraser (1951, 1959) who also deals with the alder flies, snake flies and scorpion flies (Orders Megaloptera and Mecoptera, see below).

Order Megaloptera (Alder flies, Snake flies)

Morphology: This order shares a number of characters with the "true" lacewings (see above). Adults have two pairs of similar wings with complex venation, long antennae, large compound eyes and an absence of any abdominal tails. The snake flies (family Raphidiidae; genus Raphidia*) are distinguished by their elongated prothorax, and the long egg-laying apparatus (ovipositor) in females. The presence of a pigmented spot on the forewing (the pterostigma) will also help to distinguish them from the other group in this order, the alder flies (family Sialidae). The larvae also possess a characteristic prothorax but are otherwise dissimilar from the adults. Unusually for insects which undergo full metamorphosis, the short-lived pupal stage is also active. Snake fly larvae (and pupae) differ from the lacewing larvae in having biting rather than sucking mouthparts and in having short antennae. The alder flies also have a characteristic prothorax, but are distinct from the lacewings in lacking the forked venation on wing margins. There is no pterostigma on the forewings. The larvae are aquatic.*

Ecology: Adult snake flies (4 British species) occur in wooded areas throughout Britain, usually in very thick vegetation, and near rivers and streams. They are active daytime predators, feeding on aphids and other small insects during the spring and early summer. The larvae live under bark (in beetle burrows) and feed on beetle larvae. The adult alder flies (3 spp.), which live for a few days only, are most often found near water, basking in the sunshine in late-spring to early-summer. They may feed on nectar, if at all. The larvae are aquatic predators.

Further details for identification and biology of alder flies and snake flies are given in Fraser (1959).

Order Mecoptera (Scorpion flies and Snow fleas)

Morphology: The head of adults is extended downwards into a characteristic "beak". There are two groups—the winged scorpion flies (three species belonging to the genus Panorpa) and the wingless snow fleas (one species, Boreus hyemalis). The panorpids possess two pairs of similar wings and the males have a sting-like extension to their abdomen. Although this gives the group its name it is entirely harmless, and is missing from females. The early larval stages which are active have eight pairs of abdominal "false" legs in addition to their "true" jointed thoracic legs, but these are thought to degenerate in the later stages which are exclusively earth-dwelling. The adult snow fleas are small (less than 3 mm in length) and wingless, moving by running rapidly, or jumping. Their larvae are never free-living (see below).

Ecology: The winged panorpid scorpion flies (3 spp.) are found mainly in the spring and summer, often sunning themselves in or around thickets and hedgerows—dense brambles and nettles are particularly favoured. They are scavengers, feeding on plant juices as well as dead insects and other carrion. Eggs are laid in crevices in the soil, and the active first-stage larva makes it way deeper into the earth or litter. The larvae are thought to be scavengers. The snow fleas (1 spp.) are also active during the daytime, particularly in the late autumn and winter—hence the group's name. They are most common in damp, mossy areas and their larvae spend all of their time in moss, below the surface. The snow fleas, adults and larvae, appear to feed exclusively on moss, the larvae and pupae being found in small cavities under the surface of the vegetation.

Fraser (1959) gives further details for identifications and biology.

Order Lepidoptera (Moths and Butterflies)

Morphology: A very large and diverse group. Adults usually have two pairs of membranous wings, often deeply pigmented and covered in scales. The scales are sparsely distributed between hairs in some groups. Antennae are mostly long, and mouthparts adapted for sucking—the proboscis being long, and often curved or tightly rolled under the body. Some adult members, of the families Nymphalidae, Satyridae and Riodinidae in particular, have greatly reduced forelegs and may appear to have only four legs, rather than six. Some moths have lost their mouthparts, and females of others may be wingless. Metamorphosis is complete, with larvae (caterpillars) bearing no resemblance to adults. Some live in cases constructed from silk and vegetational debris; these are known as "bagworms", mainly belonging to the family Psychidae, and easily separated from other case-forming insect larvae by the presence of abdominal prolegs. In general, caterpillars may have jointed thoracic legs, but the number of abdominal prolegs varies between groups, from 2 to 8 pairs (including the pair on the last abdominal segment). Those without legs are usually leaf-miners.

Ecology: Approximately 2500 British species. Most adults feed on plant material, usually juices—sap or nectar. Larvae have chewing mouthparts, and are often pests; some are leaf miners, stem borers, root feeders or scavengers—the latter occurring in nests, houses or granaries. However, most larvae are active browsers on vegetation. Moths and butterflies usually hibernate as eggs or pupae, although some overwinter as larvae. Adults are found mainly in the summer but some will be found throughout the year. Adults that do hibernate are often found in houses, dark rooms or sheds.

The size of the group, and their general interest to naturalists, has generated a huge literature. However, the books by Ford (1957, 1972), Emmet (1979), Higgins & Riley (1980), Skinner (1984) and Thomas (1986) will give a wide-ranging introduction to the British Lepidoptera. The first volumes in a comprehensive series dealing with all groups have been published (Heath & Emmet, 1976, onwards). Others are in preparation.

Order Trichoptera (Caddis flies)

Morphology: Most adults are four-winged and moth-like, but are covered in minute hairs rather than scales. The long antennae, absence of a coiled proboscis, and the type of wing venation will also help to separate the caddis flies from most moths, and other groups with which they could be confused—the mayflies and alder flies in particular. Females of one rare species—Enoicyla pusilla—are wingless. Most immature larvae are exclusively aquatic, but E. pusilla is terrestrial. These larvae live in a case made of sand grains and fragments of dead plant material, measuring up to 10 mm in length, which is carried around during active periods.

Ecology: Approximately 190 British species. Most adults are found near the freshwater habitats in which development to maturity has taken place. Males may swarm, particularly toward dusk. Many are nocturnal fliers. The adults may live for several weeks, but many are short-lived and will not feed. The wingless females of E. pusilla (see above) will be encountered rarely, but are found between September and November; their terrestrial cased larvae develop through to May/June of the following year. The immatures have been found only in deciduous (e.g. oak, beech, small-leaved lime) leaf litter although they may persist amongst conifers which have been planted to replace broad-leaved trees. Rarely, they may be found up to heights of 0.5 m, amongst algae, lichens and mosses on tree trunks, especially when atmospheric humidity is high. Rare in Britain, having been recorded only from wooded areas in Worcestershire, Herefordshire and Shropshire, all within approximately 10 miles of Bewdley in the Wyre Forest. They appear to feed on soft dead vegetable matter.

The biology of the British caddis flies is reviewed by Hickin (1967) and a key to adults of the British species is given by Macan (1973).

Order Diptera (Two-winged flies)

Morphology: A huge group, displaying great structural diversity. Almost all have a single pair of wings, with the second pair modified into balancers (halteres). The presence and location of the halteres, and the form of the mouthparts (always of the sucking type, but sometimes adapted for piercing or cutting) will distinguish the Diptera from other two-winged insects: mayflies (Ephemeroptera); bugs (Hemiptera); Strepsiptera. Some parasitic or phoretic forms have lost both sets of wings. Life histories are sometimes complex, particularly in the parasites, but all larvae undergo complete metamorphosis before maturation and do not resemble the adults. The larvae never have true legs, but may have prolegs. The larvae of the more "primitive" families have a well developed head capsule whereas this has been lost in the more "advanced" groups. The latter have enclosed mouthparts which should be visible under strong light, particularly if the specimen is gently squeezed between two slides.

Ecology: It is impossible to summarise the biology of this large group (6,000+ British spp.) in the space available here. The two-winged flies occupy all terrestrial habitats as adults, and the larvae are found also in many aquatic habitats. They are found at all times of the year. All food sources are utilised, but the larvae feed primarily on decaying animal and vegetable matter.

The biology of the British diptera is described in Colyer & Hammond (1968), and further useful information is contained in the Dipterist's Handbook (Stubbs & Chandler, 1978). An up-to-date key to families is given by Unwin (1981). The hoverflies—family Syrphidae—are a group which have attracted particular interest, with the books by Stubbs & Falk (1983) and Gilbert (1986) giving wide-ranging introductions to ecology and identification in this group. Volumes 9 and 10 of the "Handbooks for the Identification of British insects" series, published by the Royal Entomological Society of London, deal with individual families of diptera and a full list is available on request from the Society at 41 Queens Gate, London SW7.

Order Siphonaptera (Fleas)

Morphology: The adult fleas are small (less than 7 mm long), wingless external parasites of vertebrates, which are strongly flattened from side to side. The non-parasitic larvae undergo complete metamorphosis. They are worm-like, sometimes reaching 4 mm in length, and may resemble some dipteran larvae (see notes above). Flea larvae are always restricted to the nests of their prospective hosts.

Ecology: The 56 British species are all blood-sucking external parasites as adults, using a wide range of hosts. However, most species are associated with a particular host. Free-living adults will be taken usually in the vicinity of the dead host (or in its nest), and are more likely to leave the protection of the host's body in warmer weather. Fleas are active throughout the year, often jumping considerable distances when disturbed. The free-living larvae feed on detritus in the hosts' nests.

Further details for biology and identification are given by Smit (1957) and George (1969).

Order Hymenoptera (Sawflies, Bees, Ants and Wasps)

An extremely large and varied group of four-winged (occasionally wingless) insects consisting of two contrasting sub-orders which are best considered apart. The Symphyta *(wood wasps and sawflies: 480+ British spp.) and* Apocrita *(all bees, ants and wasps, plus many parasitic groups; 5000+ British spp.) are distinguished by the presence of a waist in the Apocrita. It is absent in the sawflies.*

Symphyta

*Morphology: Vary greatly in size, up to 40 mm. Four-winged, lacking a constricted waist. The wings may be reduced in some rare cases, but most often have complex venation with at least three closed cells in the forewings. Females may have obvious "stings" (the ovipositors) which are used for drilling the wood in which eggs are laid—hence their common name, the wood-wasps. The larvae may be free-living, whilst others are tunnellers in leaves and stems or develop inside Rosaceae fruits, galls or leaf rolls. The galls and leaf rolls are particularly common on willows (*Salix *spp.). The free-living larvae resemble caterpillars but have more abdominal prolegs, at least six pairs, and may be large, up to 25 mm. The enclosed larvae have lost the prolegs and may be confused with some beetle larvae.*

Ecology: Adult sawflies feed mainly on pollen or honeydew, but some are predators. They are found on vegetation in a wide range of habitats, from spring through to late autumn. Most larvae are herbivorous, feeding primarily on one particular foodplant.

Apocrita

Morphology: This group includes over 5000 parasitic species (the Parasitica) as well as 600+ species belonging to the non-parasitic solitary and social groups—ants, bees and wasps (the Aculeata). Several large families combine both lifestyles. There is considerable variation in morphology and habit. However, all share one common feature—the constricted waist. The majority of adults have four-wings, but many are wingless. The females of many parasitic species have long sting-like ovipositors whereas the social groups do not. Other differences occur in the wing venation; this can be quite complex in some insects but is almost totally absent in others. The larvae are never free-living and are legless, usually without any well-defined head capsule.

Ecology: The Apocrita display a great range of lifestyles. It includes many parasitic species, the gall-forming wasps, the solitary hunting wasps and bees, and the colony-forming social bees, ants and wasps. With the exception of the gall wasps and bees, the aculeate larvae are always fed on the bodies of invertebrates, often the larvae of other insect groups. In parasitic species the eggs are laid in, or near, the body of the host, but in hunting species the prey is carried to a nest. Some parasitic species attack other parasites—a phenomenon known as hyperparasitism. The adults feed mainly on nectar and honeydew, but some of the parasitic species have been known to feed on the hosts whilst ovipositing.

Many books deal with the biology of this vast group, but none is comprehensive in itself; Richards (1977) includes a key to the families of all Hymenoptera, and AIDGAP keys to Hymenopteran families and genera of Symphyta are in preparation. Keys by Yeo & Corbet (1983) (species of solitary wasps) and Willmer (1985) (genera of all aculeates—the bees, ants and wasps) take identification further. Brian (1977) deals with ants; Edwards (1980), with social wasps; Prŷs-Jones & Corbet (1987) with bumblebees. All include full lists of references for these groups. Volumes 6, 7 and 8 of the Royal Entomological Society's handbooks series will take identification to species level in some families. Useful information is also given in the Hymenopterist's Handbook (Cooper, 1945).

Order Coleoptera (Beetles)

Morphology: A huge order, with approximately 4000 species in Britain. The vast majority have two pairs of wings when mature, with the first pair modified into hardened wing cases (the elytra) which meet down the midline of the upper abdomen. The rove beetles, and some other groups, are characterised by having truncated elytra which only partly cover the abdomen. These may be confused with earwigs (Dermaptera) but never have anal pincers. Another common mistake is to identify bugs (Hemiptera) as beetles, and vice versa. The two groups can be separated by their mouthparts; beetles are always of the biting form, with well developed jaws and segmented palps, whereas those of the bugs are almost always modified into sucking tubes which are held under the body, and lacking segmented palps. Some adult beetles, the female "glow worm" for example, are completely wingless. These may be mistaken for larvae of other beetles and, occasionally, lacewings (Neuroptera; p. 757). However, the mouthparts, five-segmented tarsi and full complement of 11 antennal segments will distinguish the adult beetles. The beetle larvae undergo complete metamorphosis, but can vary between active free-living forms with well-developed legs to others which are maggot-like and lack any appendages. The latter are rarely free-living, usually tunnelling in stems and leaves or in the underground nests of insect hosts on whose larvae they feed.

Ecology: Beetles occupy all terrestrial, and most aquatic, habitats, and utilise all food sources. Many are active predators, whilst others are entirely herbivorous. Scavengers are also well represented. The adults can be found at any time of the year. The larvae display a similar range of habits. Although the more primitive forms are active predators many others are not free-living, spending their existence tunnelling in stems and leaves, or in the soil, feeding on plant material. The larvae of some parasitic species adopt both lifestyles during their development. After eggs are laid by the adults, the first stage larvae are active and search for the nest of a host. Having found a suitable nest the larvae moult, becoming increasingly maggot-like until they complete their development by metamorphosing into mature adults. This cycle of "regressive" development is known as hypermetamorphosis.

Identification and reviews of the biology of beetles are given by Linssen (1959), Walsh & Dibb (1974), Crowson (1981) and Harde & Hammond (1984). The AIDGAP key by Unwin (1984) takes identification of adults to family level. The only comprehensive work enabling identification of British beetles to species level is Joy (1932) but this is now out-dated. Volumes 4 and 5 of the Royal Entomological Society's handbooks series contain specific keys for a number of families. Walsh & Dibb (1975) provide a good introduction to practical work with the Coleoptera.

Order Strepsiptera

Morphology: The free-living male is less than 3 mm long, has one pair of wings, with the front wings reduced to club-shaped halteres. Distinctive, branched antennae. The wings are very broad, and have reduced venation. The female developes in the host (see below) and is worm-like. Eggs and larvae also develop within hosts, but may have a short-lived free-living stage shortly after hatching.

Ecology: Sixteen British species. All are parasites, mainly on Hymenoptera but also on Hemiptera. Active free-living Strepsipteran larvae emerge from their adult host and may be taken on flowers, etc. whilst waiting to attach to another adult which will be used to transport them back to a nest where they eventually parasitise the host species' larvae. Although present in large numbers shortly after hatching, the Strepsipteran larvae are only rarely found.

Very little information is available for this group but Unwin (1984) takes identification of adults to family level and Linssen (1959) gives more details on life-history, etc.

Phylum MOLLUSCA
Class Gastropoda

Two Orders are represented in British terrestrial habitats: Pulmonata and Prosobranchia. The former have lungs and are adapted for a terrestrial life, whereas most prosobranch species are gilled and more suited for an aquatic existence. Not surprisingly, of the 115 terrestrial gastropod species encountered in Britain only 2 are prosobranchs, and these can be distinguished from the pulmonate snails by their having a horny "lid"— the *operculum*—which is used to seal off the shell aperture when the animal retreats. All of the remaining species, both slugs and snails, are pulmonates. The snails are instantly recognisable from other groups of animals because of their shells, and slugs can be distinguished by their tentacles. The distinction between slugs and snails is less clear-cut. Some "snails" have very small shells, whereas one family of "slugs"—the carnivorous slugs (family Testacellidae)—has a rudimentary shell. Further details of all British species are given in Kerney & Cameron (1979), and identification to species of snails in Cameron & Redfern (1976), and slugs in Cameron et al. (1983).

ACKNOWLEDGEMENTS

Thanks are due to Dr John Crothers who administered the "testing" of a preliminary version of this guide and edited the manuscripts and proofs. Also, to the many people who took the trouble to use the key and return their comments; without their efforts the guide would undoubtedly have floundered. Dr Henry Disney scrutinised the early versions, and was supportive throughout. The fact that Indonesian fauna still fail to key out is entirely my fault. Dr David Harding and Mr R. G. Middleton permitted me to use and copy from their drawings of the elusive cased caddis fly larva. Thanks also to Dr David Sheppard and the Nature Conservancy Council for lending me a specimen of a cased beetle larva. Lastly, I am grateful to the anonymous trust and the Field Studies Council for the financial and administrative support which has enabled the AIDGAP project to survive.

REFERENCES

AGUILAR, J., DOMMANGET, J.-L., and PRÉCHAC. (1986). *A field guide to the Dragonflies of Britain, Europe and North Africa*. Collins, London.

ARTHUR, D. R. (1963). *British Ticks*. Butterworths, London.

BALL, I. R. and REYNOLDSON, T. B. (1981). *British Planarians*. Synopses of the British Fauna (New Series) No. 19. Linnean Society of London.

BLOWER, J. G. (1985). *Millipedes*. Synopses of the British Fauna (New Series) No. 35. Linnean Society of London.

BRIAN, M. V. (1977). *Ants*. New Naturalists Series. Collins, London.

BRINDLE, A. (1977). British earwigs. *Entomologist's Gazette 28*.

BRISTOWE, W. S. (1958). *The world of spiders*. New Naturalist series. Collins, London.

BROWN, V. K. (1983). *Grasshoppers*. Cambridge University Press.

CAMERON, R. A. D., EVERSHAM, B. and JACKSON, N. (1983). A field guide to the slugs of the British Isles. *Field Studies*, **5**, 807–824. An AIDGAP Key.

CAMERON, R. A. D. and REDFERN, M. (1976). *British land snails*. Synopses of the British Fauna (New series). Linnean Society, London.

CLAY, T. (1969). A key to the genera of Menoponidae (Amblycera: Mallophaga: Insecta). *Bulletin of the British Museum (Natural History) (Ent.) 24*: 1–26.

CLAY, T. (1970). The Amblycera (Phthiraptera: Insecta). *Bulletin of the British Museum (Natural History) (Ent.) 25*: 75–98.

CHINERY, M. (1986). *A field guide to the insects of Britain and Western Europe*. Collins, London.

CLOUDSLEY-THOMPSON, J. L. and SANKEY, J. (1961). *Land Invertebrates*. Methuen & Co. Ltd., London.

COLYER, C. N. and HAMMOND, C. O. (1968). *Flies of the British Isles* (2nd ed.). Wayside and Woodland Series. Frederick Warne & Co. Ltd, London.

COOPER, B. A. (Ed.) (1945). *The Hymenopterist's Handbook*. Reprinted 1969. Amateur Entomologists' Society.

CORBET, P. S., LONGFIELD, C. and MOORE, N. W. (1960). *Dragonflies*. New Naturalist Series. Collins, London.

CROWSON, R. A. (1981). *The Biology of the Coleoptera*. Academic Press, London.

DELANEY, M. J. (1954). *Thysanura and Diplura*. Handbooks for the Identification of British Insects. Vol. 1, Part 2. Royal Entomological Society of London.

EASON, E. H. (1964). *Centipedes of the British Isles*. Frederick Warne & Co. Ltd., London.

EDWARDS, R. (1980). *Social Wasps*. Rentokil Library, East Grinstead.

EDWARDS, C. A. and LOFTY, J. R. (1972). *The biology of earthworms* (2nd ed.). Chapman & Hall, London.

ELLIOT, J. M. and HUMPESCH, U. H. (1983). *A key to the adults of the British Ephemeroptera*. Scientific Publication No. 47, Freshwater Biological Association.

ELLIOT, J. M. and MANN, K. H. (1979). *A key to the British freshwater leeches*. Scientific Publication No. 40, Freshwater Biological Association.

EMMET, A. M. (1979). *A Field Guide to the smaller British Lepidoptera*. British Entomological and Natural History Society, London.

EVANS, G. O. and BROWNING, E. B. (1954). *Pseudoscorpiones*. Synopses of the British Fauna (Old Series) No. 10. Linnean Society of London.

EVANS, G. O., SHEALS, J. G. and MACFARLANE, D. (1961). *The terrestrial Acari of the British Isles. An introduction to their morphology, biology and classification. Vol. 1. Introduction and biology*. British Museum (Natural History), London.

FERRIS, G. F. (1961). *The sucking lice*. Pacific Coast Entomological Society, San Francisco.

FJELLBERG, A. (1982). *Identification keys to Norwegian Collembola*. Norsk Entomologisk, Forening.

FORD, E. B. (1957). *Butterflies* (3rd ed.). New Naturalist Series No. 1. Collins, London.

FORD, E. B. (1972). *Moths* (3rd ed.). New Naturalist Series No. 30. Collins, London.

FRASER, F. C. (1951). *Collecting Lacewings*. Revised 1976. Amateur Entomologist's Society leaflet No. 22.

FRASER, F. C. (1959). *Mecoptera, Megaloptera, Neuroptera*. Handbooks for the Identification of British Insects. Vol. 1 (12 & 13). Royal Entomological Society of London.

GEORGE, R. S. (1969). *Collecting Fleas*. Amateur Entomologist's Society leaflet No. 29.

GIBBONS, Bob (1986). *Dragonflies and Damselflies of Britain and Northern Europe*. Country Life Guides, Hamlyn, London.

GIBSON, R. (1982). *British Nemerteans*. Synopses of the British Fauna (New Series). Linnean Society, London.

GILBERT, F. S. (1986). *Hoverflies*. Naturalists' Handbooks, Cambridge University Press, Cambridge.

GISIN, H. (1960). *Collembolenfaunas Europas*. Museum d'Histoire Naturelle, Geneva (German text).

GOODEY, T. (1963). *Soil and Freshwater Nematodes*. 2nd Ed (revised by J. B. Goodey). Methuen, London.

GREEN, E. E. (1922). A Brief Review of the Indigenous Coccidae of the British Islands. *South London Entomological and Natural History Society, Proceedings 1922*: 12–25.

GURNEY, R. (1931). *British Freshwater Copepods*. Vol's I, II and III. Ray Society, London.

HAMMOND, C. O. (1985). *The Dragonflies of the British Isles* (2nd ed.). Harley Books, Colchester.

HARDE, K. W. and HAMMOND, P. W. (1984). *A Field Guide in Colour to Beetles*. Octopus Books, London.

HARDING, J. P. and SMITH, W. A. (1960). *A key to the British Freshwater Cyclopoid and Calanoid Copepods*. Scientific Publication No. 18, Freshwater Biological Association.

HARDING, P. T. and SUTTON, S. L. (1985). *Woodlice in Britain and Ireland: distribution and habitat*. Institute of Terrestrial Ecology, Monks Wood, Huntingdon.

HEATH, J. and EMMET, A. M. (eds) (1976). *The moths and butterflies of Great Britain and Ireland*. 11 volumes, 4 completed. Harley Books, Colchester.

HICKIN, N. E. (1967). *Caddis Larvae*. Hutchinson, London.

HIGGINS, L. G. and RILEY, N. D. (1980). *A field guide to the butterflies of Britain and Europe* (4th ed.). Collins, London.

HINCKS, W. D. (1956). *Dermaptera and Orthoptera*. Handbooks for the Identification of British Insects, Vol. 1, Part 5. Royal Entomological Society of London.

HYNES, H. B. N. (1977). *A key to the adults and nymphs of the British stoneflies*. Scientific Publication No. 17 (3rd Ed.). Freshwater Biological Association.

IMMS, A. D. (1977). *A general textbook of entomology* (11th ed., revised by O. W. Richards & R. G. Davies). Methuen & Co Ltd, London.

JACKSON, R. N. and RAW, F. (1966). *Life in the Soil*. Institute of Biology Studies in Biology, No. 2., Arnold, London.

JONES, Dick (1984). *The Country Life Guide to Spiders of Britain and Northern Europe*. Country Life Books (Newnes), London.

JOY, N. H. (1932). *A Practical Handbook of British Beetles* (2 vols). Reprinted in 1976 by E. W. Classey Ltd, Faringdon, Oxfordshire.

KEEN, D. (1977). *Collecting and studying Dragonflies*. Amateur Entomologist's Society leaflet No. 12.

KEVAN, D. K. McE. (1962). *Soil Animals*. H. F. & G. Witherby Ltd, London.

KERNEY, M. P. and CAMERON, R. A. D. (1979). *A Field Guide to the Land Snails of Britain and North-west Europe*. Collins, London.

LEWIS, J. G. E. (1981). *The biology of Centipedes*. Cambridge University Press, Cambridge.

LEWIS, T. (1973). *Thrips*. Academic Press, London.

LINCOLN, R. J. (1979). *British Marine Amphipoda: Gammaridea*. British Museum (Natural History), London.

LINSSEN, R. F. (1959). *Beetles of the British Isles* (2 volumes). Frederick Warne & Co. Ltd., London.

LOCKET, G. H. and MILLEDGE, A. F. (1951–53). *British Spiders, Vols 1 & 2*. Ray Society, London.

LOCKET, G. H., MILLEDGE, A. F. and MERRETT, P. (1974). *British Spiders, Vol. 3*. Ray Society, London.

MACAN, T. T. (1969). *The study of mayflies (Ephemeroptera)*. Amateur Entomologist's Society leaflet No. 31.

MACAN, T. T. (1973). *A key to the adults of the British Trichoptera*. Scientific Publication No. 28, Freshwater Biological Association.

MACAN, T. T. (1982). The study of Stoneflies, Mayflies and Caddis Flies. *The Amateur Entomologist 17*.

MANN, K. H. (1962). *Leeches. Their structure, physiology, ecology and embryology*. Pergamon Press, London.

MANN, K. H. (1964). *A key to the British Freshwater leeches with notes on their ecology*. Scientific Publication No. 28, Freshwater Biological Association.

MARSHALL, J. and HAES, C. (in prep.). *Grasshoppers and allied insects of Great Britain and Ireland*. Harley Books, Colchester.

MCGEERY, ANDREW (1986). *A complete guide to British Dragonflies*. Jonathan Cape, London.

MOUND, L. A., MORISON, G. D., PITKIN, B. R. and PALMER, J. M. (1976). *Thysanoptera*. Handbooks for the Identification of British Insects. Vol. 1, part 11. Royal Entomological Society of London.

NEW, T. R. (1974). *Psocoptera*. Handbooks for the Identification of British Insects. Vol. 1, part 7. Royal Entomological Society of London.

NOSEK, J. (1973). *The European Protura, their taxonomy, ecology and distribution with keys for determination*. Museum d'Histoire Naturelle, Geneva (English text).

O'CONNOR, F. B. (1967). The Enchytraeidae. In *Soil Biology* (A. Burges & F. Raw, eds), pp. 212–257. Academic Press, London.

PANTIN, C. F. A. (1969). The genus *Geonemertes*. *Bulletin of the British Museum (Natural History) (Zoology)*, 18: 263–310.

PRŶS-JONES, O. E. and CORBET, S. A. (1987). *Bumblebees*. Naturalists' Handbooks, Cambridge University Press, Cambridge.

RAGGE, D. R. (1965). *Grasshoppers, Crickets and Cockroaches of the British Isles*. Wayside and Woodland Series. Frederick Warne & Co. Ltd., London.

RICHARDS, O. W. (1977). *Hymenoptera: Introduction and key to the families*. Handbooks for the Identification of British Insects. Vol. 6, part 1, 2nd edition. Royal Entomological Society of London.

ROBERTS, M. J. (1985; 1987). *The spiders of Great Britain and Ireland*. Harley Books, Colchester.

SANKEY, J. H. P. and SAVORY, T. H. (1974). *British harvestmen*. Synopses of the British Fauna (New Series) No. 4. Linnean Society, London.

SIMS, R. W. and GERARD, B. M. (1985). *Earthworms*. Synopses of the British Fauna (New Series) No. 31. Linnean Society, London.

SKIDMORE, P. (1985). Insects of the cowdung community. AIDGAP Test Version.

SKINNER (1984). *Moths of the British Isles*. Viking Books, London.

SMIT, F. G. A. M. (1957), *Siphonaptera*. Handbooks for the Identification of British Insects. Vol. 1, part 16. Royal Entomological Society of London.

STUBBS, A. and CHANDLER, P. (1978). *A Dipterists' Handbook*. The Amateur Entomologist's Society.

STUBBS, A. E. and FALK, S. J. (1983). *British Hoverflies—an Illustrated Identification Guide*. British Entomological and Natural History Society, London.

SOUTHWOOD, T. R. E. and LESTON, D. (1959). *Land and water bugs of the British Isles*. Wayside and Woodland Series. Frederick Warne & Co. Ltd., London.

SUTTON, S. L. (1972). *Woodlice*. Ginn & Co., London.

THOMAS, J. A. (1986). *The RSNC guide to Butterflies of the British Isles*. Guild Publishing, London.

UNWIN, D. M. (1981). A key to the families of British Diptera. *Field Studies*, 5(3): 513–544. An AIDGAP key.

UNWIN, D. M. (1984). A key to the families of British Coleoptera and Strepsiptera. *Field Studies*, 6(1): 149–197. An AIDGAP key.

WALSH, G. B. and DIBB, J. R. (1953: 1975). *A Coleopterist's Handbook*. First printed 1953, revised by Cooter, J. and Cribb, P. W. (1975). Amateur Entomologist's Society, Hanworth, Middlesex.

WANLESS, F. R. (1977). On the occurrence of the scorpion *Euscorpius flavicaudis* (DeGeer) at Sheerness Port, Isle of Sheppey, Kent. *Bulletin of the British Arachnological Society* 4, 74–76.

WILLMER, P. (1985). Bees, ants and wasps. A key to the genera of the British Aculeates. *Occasional Publication No. 7*, Field Studies Council. An AIDGAP key.

YEO, P. F. and CORBET, S. A. (1983). *Solitary Wasps*. Cambridge University Press.

INDEX

The index shows where groups of animals key out followed by the page number where the morphological and ecological notes can be found (in bold print).